INFLUENCE

HISTORICAL EVENTS

1803, Louisiana Purchase. 1804, Lewis & Clark. 1805, Austerlitz; Napoleon, master of Europe. 1812, War of 1812; superiority of American-made ships. 1815, Waterloo. 1817, Erie Canal begun. 1819, Queen Victoria born. 1821, Missouri 5th new state in 6 years. 1825, Erie Canal opens up the West. 1830, Ohio has more people than Massachusetts. 1834, McCormick invents the reaper. 1836, fall of the Alamo. 1837, Queen Victoria's coronation. 1839, screw propeller used on ships. 1845, Duncan Phyfe closes New York shop. 1846, Mexican War. 1849, California Gold Rush. 1852, *Uncle Tom's Cabin*. 1855, Whitman's *Leaves of Grass*. 1857, Otis invents the elevator. 1858, Lincoln-Douglas debates. 1859, John Brown's Raid. 1861, Fort Sumter fired on. 1865, Lincoln assassinated. 1866, Atlantic cable laid. 1868, Eastlake's *Hints on Household Taste*. 1869, Union-Pacific Railroad completed. 1870, corruption under Grant; Rockefeller forms Standard Oil Trust. 1872, corruption under Boss Tweed. 1875, Mark Twain's *Tom Sawyer*. 1876, Centennial Exposition; Custer's last stand. 1879, Edison invents electric light. 1885, immigration from northern Europe to the West. 1886, American Federation of Labor. 1888, first electric trolley cars. 1892, Homestead strike against Carnegie Steel. 1895, Elbert Hubbard starts pr 1896, Klondike gold rush; Bryan's "Reme San Ju launch dies. 1 1908, Woman Suffrage in 12 states. 1915, fifteen million autos on the road.

JACOBEAN 1870–1880

ORIENTAL (TURKISH) 1875 TO 1900

MISSION 1895–1910

GOLDEN OAK 1900–1915

ART NOUVEAU 1895–1910

THE NEW
ANTIQUES

Other books by George Grotz

FROM GUNK TO GLOW
THE FURNITURE DOCTOR
ANTIQUES YOU CAN DECORATE WITH
INSTANT FURNITURE REFINISHING
   AND OTHER CRAFTY PRACTICES
STAINING AND FINISHING UNFINISHED
   FURNITURE AND OTHER NAKED WOODS
DECORATING FURNITURE WITH
   A LITTLE BIT OF CLASS

The New Antiques:

KNOWING AND BUYING VICTORIAN FURNITURE

GEORGE GROTZ

REVISED EDITION, WITH CURRENT
PRICE GUIDE IN BACK PAGES

DOUBLEDAY & COMPANY, INC.

GARDEN CITY, NEW YORK

It was in 1812 that a famous
English critic wrote: "In the
four quarters of the globe, who
reads an American book, or
goes to an American play, or
looks at an American picture
or statue?"

Well, things have been looking up since then, fella. And
that's what this book is really
all about.

Library of Congress Catalog Card Number 73–78710

Copyright © 1963, 1964, 1970 by George Grotz

CONTENTS

PART III APPENDIX

A guided tour behind the scenes with the author and
his infamous Uncle George. An irreverent but practical guide for anyone who has ever thought about going
into the antique business.

"SEE PRICE GUIDE
IN BACK OF BOOK"

*Explaining our new way of giving prices
and predictions in a separate section in
the back of the book (page 211), and
some new thinking on why the value of
everything Victorian will continue to
skyrocket.*

In the six years since this book was originally published, the prices of everything in it have doubled, tripled, or quadrupled and in some cases even quintupled and more.

And since my esteemed publishers see a continuing market for this book as a reference work, they have asked me to take the current market prices and predictions out of the individual captions (where they were in the first edition) and put all that information on a few pages in the back of the book. This, I am informed, will make it much more economical to keep updating that information in future editions and therefore will make future editions more likely—a consummation devoutly to be wished by any poor struggling author.

Now let me explain my theory about why Victoriana has risen so much in the last five years. To begin with, it is easy to understand that, since all antiques exist in a limited quantity, their market price in dollars will gradually rise with inflation, to which all mankind seems to be committed except in brief periods of depression. Also, since all antiques exist in a limited number, our increasing population makes them gradually more rare and therefore gradually more valuable. In the last six years the value of all antiques has risen about twenty per cent—which is not quite the increase you would have gotten in the last six years if you had invested your money in savings bonds. (However, you get to use and look at your antiques.)

But the market prices of the pieces illustrated in this book have all risen at least one hundred per cent (doubled), and the majority have done even better than that. Many of the pieces in the later styles have gone from $5 to $25. Especially desirable pieces such as desks have risen from $75 to $175 and $225. And even in an older style such as Empire we find $35 chairs going to $80. Obviously such increases must be caused by something more than gradual inflation and population expansion.

My theory is this: The spread of electronic communication television—has rapidly made us more sophisticated. We see everything, and as a result we have come to see that Victorian antiques (1) are more interesting in their variety and design than other antiques are, and (2) they have more significance to us because their history is uniquely American.

By their being uniquely American, I mean that of all the styles of so-called American antiques, the Victorian styles are the only ones that were not developed from European styles and that were made here only.

For instance, it is silly to call pieces in the styles of Queen Anne, Chippendale, Hepplewhite, Adam, and Sheraton Early American antiques. They simply were English styles that were copied by cabinetmakers who had immigrated here in the early 1700s. All well and good, but still not really American. And, of course, we have to say the same of the French styles that we commonly stretch Victoriana to include. (See end-paper diagram.) However, these are only four exceptions out of the fifteen styles of Victorian. And even so, American Empire— the major one of these four styles—doesn't look much like French Empire.

This leaves us with the rest of Victorian—eleven styles and

ninety per cent of the pieces, which are truly American by virtue of having been products of the Industrial Revolution. That means that their designs were influenced and even dominated by the increasing sophistication of the machinery available to furniture manufacturers.

And that means that anyone whose line goes back only as far as having an American grandfather can identify with these styles and their relationship to the culture of their times. These antiques—from 1815 to 1915—tell the story of America's coming of age in the Industrial Revolution.

And if we need roots—who doesn't?—these Victorian antiques are the only ones that the great majority of us can turn to with any honesty. Even people whose ancestors came to this country in the 1700s had grandfathers and great-grandfathers and great-great-grandfathers here during the Victorian century.

So, *ipso facto*, the more people become aware that Victoriana is the truest American, the more they turn to preferring them and will continue to do so. Which means the boom has only started.

You mark my words. And see if I wasn't right when I come back to see you in about five more years.

For their help in revising this edition, I want to give special thanks to Bob Jenkins of Leonard's Antiques, Inc., on Route 44 in Seekonk, Massachusetts, and the two Jerrys of Victoria House on the corner of Perry and Hudson streets in New York City. And, as always, my thanks to the many helpful dealers in the Bucks County Antique Dealers Association and the Southern New England Antique Dealers Association. (You can find Victorian antiques in every city and hamlet in the United States—and good luck to you!—but these are the areas where extensive trading establishes the base prices for the whole country. You will find specific references to this situation in the Price Guide in the back of this book.)

WHAT THIS BOOK IS ABOUT

Well, here you are with another book and another preface to get through. Frankly I'm against prefaces. But I am told by my betters that there is a small segment of our population that insists on being told what a book is about before they read it. They could, of course, look at the table of contents. But then, I notice that hardly anybody ever does that either. I know because I have sold books, and I have watched how people look them over.

First, they weigh the book in their hands to get the feel of it. As if it were a hammer or something. I don't know why they do this. Then they strum through the pages from back to front. I think they do this to see if anyone has left any old five-dollar bills in them. Then they read pages haphazardly. And if the author is lucky enough to have written something that interests them on that page, they close the book and look at the jacket to see what the title is. Finally, they read the blurb. Here they also see what the price is. And then the decision is made. They then either start fishing in their pocketbooks for their money or put the book back on the counter with a pursed mouth and a slight frown.

But enough of these reflections, and down to the job of telling you wonderful preface reader, if you are still with me, what this book is supposed to be about.

To begin with, if you are looking for a $3500 Chippendale secretary, the book can't help you at all. Put it quietly back on the counter and forget the whole thing.

On the other hand, if you are one of us common people who are interested in the kind of furniture that comes up at country auctions and that you find in out-of-the-city antique shops—well, then maybe this book can be of some use to you.

It is the first one ever put together to help you to identify and price the only kind of antique furniture that we ordinary folk ever see for sale and can afford to buy.

This is the furniture of the latest "wave" of antiques—not priceless works of art, but pieces that were made after 1830. This furniture has been zooming up in popularity (and price) in the last thirty years. And it still has a long way to go—in popularity *and price*—for two reasons:

First, because of its emotional and personal connotations. It reminds us all of days gone by and the way things were (or at least the way we like to think they were) when our grand-fathers and great-grandfathers were running a saner world.

Secondly, because this furniture was designed and made in America. It tells the story of our nation's struggle to get out from under the cultural influence of Europe, to work out our own ideas, to express the way we feel, to make things the way we think they should be made, with our mastery of tools and our mechanical ingenuity.

I have divided this book into three parts. Part I tells the story of this furniture—the first in the history of the world ever produced by a technological civilization. It also gives some practical hints on decorating with Victorian.

Part II is a guide to differentiating the various styles—when possible, because they sometimes got so mixed up with each other that no one will ever be able to unscramble them. Part II also tells how to refinish Victorian pieces.

In Part III, I try to tell how the antique business works—and a business, a big one, it is. And since I believe that every-one should be in business for himself, I have tried to make it a sort of guide for anyone who has toyed with the idea of someday having a little antique shop in the country. (Go ahead. You'll starve to death, but it's an awful lot of fun!)

SOURCES AND THANK-YOUS

To some people and books.

The first person to help with this book was Joe Patrick, world traveler, *bon vivant*, and avid collector of Victoriana. In the enormous storeroom behind his shop in Provincetown ("Treasures and Trash") he let me photograph more than a hundred representative pieces of Victorian furniture. The tip of Cape Cod may seem like a strange place to find Victoriana, but as Joe pointed out, it is a gold mine. The reason is that the town had its heyday back when whaling was a big industry. At one time, some forty piers stuck out into the harbor to service the whaling fleet. And those were the days when the houses were built and the furniture packed into them—practically all of which is still there. Joe, incidentally, is not an Irishman, as the name might suggest to some, but of Portuguese descent—as are most of the natives of Provincetown. These descendants of the men who sailed the whaling boats still carry on a flourishing fishing industry.

Also of inestimable help was "Cookie" Harpin, well known in the antique business as "Trader Bob Harpin," under which pseudonym she has run ads in *Hobbies* magazine for years. It is wonderful to listen to her over the phone when she switches from her own voice to the deep baritone of her creation. People who aren't in on the secret are fooled every time.

Cookie supplied me with much of the information in this book about which pieces are both available and in popular demand. The Harpins, in West Warwick, R.I., have been leading dealers in Victoriana for a long time. If they haven't got it—which is unusual—Bob knows where to find it.

Bob Eldred, the famous auctioneer on Cape Cod, was of help in getting me started by giving me the names of the large dealers in Victorian in New England and the Middle West.

The same sort of information was also given by the editors of *The Antiques Dealer**—the magazine in which the wholesalers of antiques advertise to the trade.

Much information also came from the advertisements of dealers in two other important magazines: *Hobbies* magazine,† and *The Spinning Wheel*.‡

Very few books even mention Victorian furniture, and only one significant book is devoted entirely to the subject—at that, it covers only the earlier styles of what we now consider to be the Victorian Era. This is Thomas H. Ormsbee's *Field Guide to Early American Furniture*.** It is out of print, however, and cannot even be bought in secondhand book stores, it is so treasured by those collectors who happen to have a copy. Nor is it in many libraries. So the only way to get a copy is to beg, borrow, or steal it, and the method I used to get mine is a secret I propose to carry to the grave.

As to the meaning of Victorian furniture and hints about the histories of the various styles, two other books were of great help in evolving the separation of the styles and grouping them into the three divisions or strains of influence.

The first was John A. Kouwenhoven's *Made in America— the Arts in Modern Civilization*,†† a paper-back edition that is truly a gem of fundamental historical research into the culture of the Victorian Era. It traces development of American design in machinery, architecture, the fine arts, movies.

---

* 101 Springfield Ave., Summit, N.J.
† 1006 South Michigan Ave., Chicago, Illinois 60605.
‡ Taneytown, Md.
** Little, Brown & Co., 1951.
†† Doubleday & Company, Inc., Anchor A300, 1962.

It shows how American ideas "inevitably triumphed over the cultural heritage of Europe because of their validity and vitality."

Along the same lines, but stressing the parts played by individuals, is *The Tastemakers** by Russell Lynes. It is a very entertaining and instructive book which no one interested in Victorian should miss reading.

Finally, my sincerest thanks to the hundred or more antique dealers I have talked to in my travels, all of whom were not only willing but eager to help.

* Harper & Brothers, 1949, clothbound. Also The Universal Library, Grosset & Dunlap, Inc.

PART I

THE MEANING OF VICTORIAN

1. A NEW PERSPECTIVE ON VICTORIAN

How the conflict between traditional craftsmanship and machine-operated tools influenced the evolution of the Victorian styles.

"Each age is a dream that is dying—or one that is coming to birth."

My wife says that I should publish this book under an assumed name. She says it will be embarrassing when people find out that she is married to an uncultured lout who would have anything to do with Victorian furniture. I know what she means. We were only in the antique business about two hours before we learned that sneering at Victorian was as fundamental as bowing low three times every time the name of Chippendale was mentioned. And since in those days there were hungry mouths to feed, we quickly learned to bow and sneer at all the appropriate times.

Of course, being new hands at the game, we also had inferiority complexes. Who were we to argue with the Established Authorities? If they said that Victorian was "stuffy," "quaint but in atrocious taste," "sometimes amusing, but basically fussy and overdecorated," "a monument to bad taste"— well, who were we to argue?

But I for one had stirrings of doubt, and they were based on two things.

In the first place, I didn't think the wild experimentation that went on in the Victorian Era was *any worse* than the bald imitation of Greek and Roman designs that were used by Chippendale, Sheraton, Adam, Phyfe, and that whole bunch. And the Established Authorities certainly considered them the greatest. Their period was called the Golden Age of Furniture Design, yet not one of them ever made a chair that a man could sit in without being afraid it would break. They all tortured wood into shapes it was never intended to go into—or made their stuff out of matchsticks.

Doubts as to how much the Established Authorities really knew began to stir a little bit. I knew I was wrong, of course, so I said nary a word.

The second reason for my doubt-stirring was history. Now, believe it or not, I graduated from a rather well-known university, where I was also exposed to some courses in history and sociology and psychology and things like that.

So it seemed to me that the furniture of any period in a country's history must have something to do with the people who lived at the time—or, as the sociologists would say, with the culture. Their furniture would have to be an expression of how they lived and felt about life. And I couldn't quite accept the idea that *all* the people who lived in this country from, say, 1830 to around 1910, were dimwits. Because when you start thinking about it, these people did some remarkable things and produced some pretty unusual stuff.

To begin with, you can go back a little bit further, even to the War of 1812. This has been called the Second War of Independence, because we had to fight the British all over again. Well, the whole thing turned out to be kind of a stalemate, which in essence meant that we won. But a notable thing occurred to make it possible for us to get even a stalemate: The Navy of our thirty-six-year-old country conclusively defeated the Navy of the British Empire on practically all the oceans of the world. (You don't believe it? Look it up in the history books!) How could this happen? Simply because our ships (far fewer than the English had) had been designed by Americans, and our designs were so greatly superior to those of the English ships that our vessels could literally sail circles around the English ones. And they did. This turns out to be a great advantage when two ships are shooting at each other.

That was only the beginning. These people were also pretty smart (especially about inventing and designing things) in a lot of other ways. For instance—and this helped a lot in our westward expansion—they invented machine-made rifles and that famous "equalizer," the Colt revolver (1848). They also invented the McCormick reaper which, for the first time in the history of the world, made it possible for food to be mass produced. And the Otis elevator, which led to the world's first skyscrapers—not to mention the steel beams that made the skyscrapers possible in the first place. And you can't leave out the Model T Ford, or the telephone, or the electric-light bulb. Or the steamboat or the cotton gin.

By around the time of the Civil War they also had invented woodworking machines—for sawing, boring, mortising, and tenoning—that popped the eyes out of the head of every European craftsman that ever saw them. As one Englishman put it in a book on the subject, Americans were just too "ignorant of the difficulties to be encountered" to know that you couldn't possibly build such machines.

All right. So there I was with stirred doubts and a fascination with Victorian furniture. But I knew I was wrong and I kept my mouth shut. (Just as an awful lot of other people kept doing, too.) Then two things happened to turn the tide.

The first was that during World War II the furniture factories of this country were switched over to making gliders and footlockers and mess-hall tables and bars for officers' clubs —and all sorts of war matériel like that. This came as a bad shock to the buyers for the furniture departments of our leading department stores. They still had their furniture departments, but they didn't have anything to sell in them. So, one by one, they "discovered" how "functional," "useful," "decorative," and "important" Victorian furniture was. Maybe they didn't really believe it, but here was something they could get by the vanload from all the junk shops in the country. There wasn't anything else available, and they could sell it like hot dogs at Coney Island. And make a wonderful profit.

False as the situation was, for the first time Victorian furniture began to get a little recognition. Also, the people who bought it were committed now to thinking it was pretty good. After all, they had paid for it, and if it wasn't any good they had been stung, and whenever anyone sneered at it, they said, "Well, we like it—you just don't appreciate it."

Eventually the war was over, and the factories got back to turning out their reproduction junk and their Danish modern, and Victorian slipped out of sight again.

Then the second thing happened. Off in their ivy-covered universities, the sociologists had gotten tired of studying the ways of aborigine tribes and the ways of Polynesian girls. For lack of anything better to do, they started looking into America's "cultural heritage." In fact, they practically invented it, because it had never occurred to anyone before that we had one, and most Americans downright resent the whole idea anyway. They give you a look askance that seems to say, "What do you think—that my grandfathers were a bunch of sissies, or something?"

Well, I'm sorry, but facts are facts. We've got this thing, whether we like it or not, and we might as well get used to it and make the most of it. You had better start liking Victorian furniture, because it is right at the middle of our you-know-what, and if you don't start liking it, you are going to be very old hat quicker than you can throw a Chippendale chair out the window.

What is it that the sociologists have been finding out? Well, it turns out that the things that Americans have been making since the unpleasantness of 1776 (and this definitely includes

Victorian furniture) are unique in history—in fact, just about the first new things since the cathedrals of the Middle Ages. And the first really new furniture since the Egyptians.

The reason for this is that the Americans of the 1800s were starting out afresh in a new country and were the first people in history to build a country with power tools. It was the Age of Mechanization. And if you are going to say that furniture made by machinery isn't as good as that made by hand, you are missing the point by a long way. They aren't even remotely the same thing, and you cannot judge the new things by standards set up by people who made the old things. It is like the old Yiddish question: Which do you like best —to spend the summer in the country, or grapes? There isn't any answer, because the two things are not comparable.

Of course, it wasn't all quite that simple. While we were filling up this country with houses and furniture and automobiles that were created by machinery and whose designs were influenced by the machinery that made them—we still remembered how things looked back in Europe and felt they should look the same.

There was a conflict between designing for machine production and a desire to reproduce the designs and styles of the past. Basically, the landed gentry stuck to the old designs because they had the strongest ties with the Old World— and they could *afford* handmade things. But the common people were too busy building railroads and settling the West to be educated to the European taste. And they certainly couldn't afford to take the Grand Tour of Europe, which among the upper classes was considered the only way to learn anything.

The result of the conflict between the handmade tradition and the influence of mechanization was that the Victorian Era starts out with direct imitations of European styles. The curvy, grape-decorated parlor furniture was directly from Louis XV. The Hitchcock chairs were merely Sheraton side chairs, modified for mass production, and colorfully decorated to appeal to the simple farm wives to whom they were sold. But gradually the influence of the machine was felt as we moved through Gothic, the squared-up Eastlake (decorations glued on), the simplicity of Golden Oak and Mission, and finally to the complete triumph of the machine in Danish modern, which could not have been conceived of except in terms of machine production. This process can be clearly seen in Part II, The Styles and Their Stories.

To be sure, Victorian furniture comes from a different time, and tastes have changed. Until recently we violently rejected Victorian—somewhat in the way children often reject the ways of their parents. But time enough has gone by to give us a little perspective. Instead of dismissing Victorian furniture as fussy and old-fashioned, we begin to see in it an expression of a way of life and an emotional character. It wasn't so bad after all.

Our Victorian grandparents and great-grandparents lived in a far surer world than ours. They knew. They knew that everybody was working in the right direction. They knew that Utopia was obtainable. They knew that God was in his heaven—and on their side. They knew that in the end things had to work out for the best of possible worlds. This is a far cry from our situation today, when we're not even sure there is going to be a world when we wake up tomorrow. And that, I imagine, is one reason why more and more people are saying, "Let's stop knocking Victorian long enough to take another look at it."

One more thing. Victorians were not all antiquarians, and American antiquarians who live entirely surrounded by the past are not the kind of people that those very ancestors were whom they worship.

The antiquarians are certainly not like Mark Twain, who wrote in *A Tramp Abroad* after a trip to the British Museum in London, "I wished that the whole Past might be swept away, and each generation be compelled to bury and destroy whatever it had produced. . . . The present is burthened too much with the past."

Nor are these antiquarians like Nathaniel Hawthorne, who in 1851 wrote in *The House of the Seven Gables*, "Shall we never get rid of this past? . . . It lies upon the Present like a giant's dead body! . . . Just think a moment and it will startle you to see what slaves we are to bygone times, —to Death, if we give the matter the right word!"

Serious people, these Victorians. Not just fussy decorators interested only in frills.

Thoreau was seeking values in those days, too, and Emerson in his essays, and Walt Whitman in his songs of the Republic.

There surely is a right use of antiques in our lives—not as an avenue of escape into the past but as a reminder of the values of the past. In this respect, to me, the antiques of the Victorian Era are far more significant than any others, for they happen to be the antiques that remind us of people who rejected the past.

2. CONSTRUCTION OF VICTORIAN

*Some background information that bears
out the sociologists' theory of the rise of
a new "machine art" in our mechanized
society.*

Considering the number of styles in which Victorian furniture comes and the fact that it spans almost a hundred years, it would seem impossible to generalize about the way it was made. But if we break the era into three parts (early, middle, and late) we notice some interesting things.

For instance, there is the difference in the woods used. *Early* Victorian—and that includes all the styles that we class under the French influence (Empire, Louis XV, Baroque, Belter)—was almost all made of mahogany.

The only significant exception is that the later Louis XV chairs and settees were sometimes made of walnut. Their manufacture hung on into the *Middle* Victorian period, when walnut became the dominant wood. The middle period includes the styles we call Gothic, Renaissance, and Eastlake.

The reason for the rise of walnut's popularity was that as the furniture industry expanded with the growth of our population, manufacturers frowned at the cost and scarcity of imported mahogany, which in those days came from Honduras and Cuba in quantities that could not nearly fill the demand. It didn't take the manufacturers long to discover that our native walnut was an excellent substitute. The fact that it was thought of as a substitute for mahogany explains why it was often tinted with red stains or coated with a finish containing a reddish mahogany pigment.

Gothic was made completely of walnut. (But if you do find any Gothic that isn't walnut, don't just write me a letter—buy it and hang onto it, because it will be very valuable. So valuable that the only way to find out its worth would be through an auction attended by the leading collectors of Victorian.)

Renaissance furniture was mostly walnut—with walnut veneers sometimes used on top of the solid wood—but occasionally cherry was used, and oak.

In the case of Eastlake, our third style of the Middle Victorian period, walnut was still used, but cherry and oak became common.

Late Victorian furniture—principally Mission and Golden Oak—was entirely of oak.

I have left out a number of styles, because they were not involved in our meaningful trend. But to complete the picture:

Jacobean Revival. Compared to the other styles, very little of this was made. It was a fad that never really caught on. However, what there was of it was almost always made of oak.

Art Nouveau. Mostly of metal. Wood didn't have the structural strength for the shapes.

Spool. The pieces of higher quality were made of maple throughout the whole period during which Spool was made. Also cherry was used in some of the better pieces. Both woods were usually stained to resemble mahogany. Many later Spool pieces were made of pine—sometimes stained, sometimes painted and decorated. This later Spool Furniture could also be classed as Cottage Furniture.

Cottage. This was mass-produced, low-priced furniture, much of it sold by mail. It was almost always made of pine, which was then painted and decorated. Scraped down and stained an antique brown, this stuff accounts for about half of the so-called Early American Primitive that is so common in antique shops.

Now, as to the machinery used, the early styles of French Influence were handmade in small shops, in which the European traditions were followed. Many of the craftsmen had come from Europe—all were trained by craftsmen who had learned their techniques in Europe. Even Belter, the great technician who worked with laminated sheets of rosewood, was born in Germany and used only hand tools and hand-operated presses.

But throughout the whole era of English influence—from Gothic all the way through Golden Oak—the use of power-driven, mass-production machinery was the key to how the furniture looked when it was finished.

From Gothic on, you find no more hand-planing marks on the bottoms of drawers. You find no more straight saw cuts resulting from the primitive reciprocal-motion saw. Rather, you find now the curved marks of the whirling circular saw, which could cut planks ten times as fast. No longer are the mortise-and-tenon joints at the sides of drawers hand-cut and often irregularly spaced. They are made now by "ganged" mortising chisels or drills.

Incidentally, contrary to what people generally think, machine-made furniture was vastly superior in strength to the handcrafted pieces that had preceded it. In the first place, harder woods could be used. Now, mahogany may be beautiful, and it is just about perfect for carving and working with hand tools. But walnut is stronger, oak many times stronger, and these woods could now be used because the machinery could work them just as fast as it could handle mahogany.

Another factor was the exactness with which the machines cut their joints. The result was tighter fits. Mortise-and-tenon joints were much easier to make than dowel joints—and far stronger.

And then there was the machine that had so much to do with the "look" of Victorian furniture: the ever-present, always-spinning wood-carving machine.

To use the machine, the operator first had to have one real, bona fide piece of carving that someone had carved by hand with his little chisels and knives. All the operator of the machine had to do was to guide the point of the stylus over the face of this master carving, by means of levers, and the whirling cutting bit would reproduce the same shape in any blank piece of wood. On top of this, by means of more levers one stylus could guide the cutting action of twenty or more cutting heads. Such machines are still in use in factories making reproductions of carved-style furniture such as Chippendale.

You can see what a world of wild surmise the invention of this machine opened up to furniture manufacturers who had never seen one before. Everybody had to have one right away, and everybody had to carve something different from the other fella's. As machines with more precision were developed, everybody had to carve something fancier and more intricate than the next fella.

Another factor was that if one fella saw another fella's chair selling really big in the market, all he had to do was go out and buy one and bring it home and put it in his own carving machine. The final development was that some manufacturers set up factories just to make carvings which the furniture makers could simply glue onto their "boxes."

Structurally, Victorian furniture was made right. It was the only furniture built with sincerity since the Jacobean period. It was built to be used and to last. It was the expression of a people who knew exactly who they were and where they were going, who never doubted that the world belonged to them and that they would succeed in making it over in their own image.

Compare the construction of Victorian furniture with, say, the fragile, matchstick construction of a Hepplewhite chair. Compare it with the way the natural straight grain of wood was tortured into unnatural curves by Chippendale, in which the legs and arms and backs of chairs are always in danger of splitting. Tree trunks grow in straight lines. To the straight-thinking Victorians, that meant square furniture. Curves? Certainly—but as part of decoration applied to the basic square structure.

For a long time now the seventeenth century has been known as the Golden Age of Furniture Design. It was the era of Chippendale, Sheraton, Hepplewhite, the Adam Brothers, Duncan Phyfe. And what did they produce? Rickety, ostentatious furniture that had nothing to do with the nature of the material it was made of or the use to which it was to be put. And they call that the Golden Age of Furniture Design? When grown-up men were making chairs that no intelligent person would take a chance on sitting on? Give me a big roomy, comfortable Victorian chair any day. (Please

understand that I am talking about the later Victorian furniture—of the second half of the era—when we had gotten over imitating European styles, and true American Victorian had emerged.)

As I write these words, I am sitting in the chair shown in the accompanying illustration. After demotion from the parlor, it was used as a kitchen chair for twenty years. It has spent another thirty summers in the rough and tumble of a seashore cottage. It has been left to weather on a front porch for many a winter. It is banged, bruised, and scraped and has about seven different colors of paint on it. But it is still almost as solid as if it had been made out of cast iron. It has never been repaired, and it will probably not need to be for another 200 years. Now, if you ask me, that is a piece of furniture. It was built with integrity, and it still has it. I get a kick out of looking at something like that. And I get a thrill from thinking that I have some sort of identity with it, that I come down from the kind of people who made furniture like that. It makes me feel that I, that all of us, maybe are good enough. Maybe we still do have a chance to make the world over the way we darn well know it ought to be.

3. DECORATING WITH VICTORIAN

*In which we forget about quaintness as
we learn to appreciate the character of
Victorian furniture.*

My wife says that what I don't know about interior decoration would fill an encyclopedia, and I guess she's right. In fact, I'm not sure I even believe in it. The way I look at it, the furniture and other things we have in the rooms we live in should be things we like to have around and are useful to our way of life. So what is the problem? Just get the stuff you like, and live with it.

Of course, this can be said in another way, namely, that your surroundings should express your personality. So people hire interior decorators to come in and express their personalities for them. Or, if you don't have any personality, the decorator will make one up for you. Would you like to be Early American? Or Italian Renaissance? Or Egyptian? Just name it and it's yours.

If anybody came into our house and tried to tell my wife how to express her personality—or that the one she has is out of style—he'd get short shrift. And if he came into what we laughingly call my "study" (the décor of which takes its motif from an old Sears, Roebuck band saw) he would very likely get himself in trouble.

Besides, I know how women go about decorating their houses. I should. I've worked (at refinishing) for enough women who never get through doing it. They clip pictures that they like out of magazines. Then they go around trying to find things that look like the things in the pictures. I know, because they are always bringing their pictures to me to show me the exact color of honey-funny pine that they want their mahogany chest of drawers turned into.

I think this is a perfectly logical procedure. The only trouble with it, as far as Victorian goes, is that you don't see many pictures that show Victorian. And I can tell you why that is, too. It's because magazines exist on the money they get from their advertisers. Very few furniture companies have started making reproductions of Victorian. They will, but it hasn't gotten very far yet.

You are going to be pretty much on your own when it comes to using Victorian furniture in your house—especially if you are original or nervy enough to use any of the later styles, the ones that came after the Civil War. So you had better have a pretty good idea of what your personality is if you are going to express it in Victorian.

The least that a book on Victorian furniture should do is to offer a few guideposts on decorating with it. And so, at great personal expense, I have interviewed some interior decorators who specialize in Victorian. (The great personal expense was for the ice-cream sodas, or whatever they were, that I had to buy them to get them talking freely.) And here are some of the ideas they brought up.

For one thing, they all thought this book might be of some help because it defines the different styles of Victorian. After all, a basic principle of interior decoration is not to mix too many styles or to use styles that come from widely varying times or culture patterns. And the lumping of fifteen different styles of furniture under the term "Victorian" has not helped. If you are going to call Eastlake and Louis XV Victorian, you are going to have a rough time getting them into the same room together.

Another point they make is that most people think of the styles of the French Influence as being more formal and suitable for use in living and dining rooms, while all the styles of English Influence strike people as being gay or light or amusing. The English styles go very well in informal rooms, party rooms, foyers, and other entrance areas.

As to the colors to use on walls, draperies, and upholstery, one of my friends points out that he never considers the dark hue of so much Victorian a troublesome factor, because he almost always bleaches it or antiques it anyway. But if you are going to leave dark Victorian in its original walnut or mahogany, they all agreed that it calls for the use of fairly strong colors in the upholstery and fairly dark walls—certainly not white or pastel walls. (I think all walls should be white—but who am I to argue with an interior decorator?)

My friends pointed out that each of the styles has a different emotional connotation and historical association. Empire carries with it the air of powdered wigs and Revolutionary times when our ties with France were strong. Louis XV does the same thing, but its curving lines and moldings are softer and more feminine. Empire is excellent for a man's study, Louis XV calls to mind the gracious but formal hostess in her drawing room.

Baroque furniture, including Belter, follows the formality of Empire and Louis XV but is more sophisticated and implies an arty, knowledgeable, and world-traveled approach to life. Also that you are rich enough to afford it.

Moving into the English Influence, if you should happen to find any Gothic—and it is very rare—the only place it won't look like a museum exhibit is in a formal country house, say on the banks of the Hudson River, where it was invented.

Renaissance, of course, is one of the most popular of the English styles and speaks of gaiety and the romantic times before and after the Civil War. It is certainly feminine, which is probably why so many women like to use it as a background for their personalities.

Eastlake is a problem child, because there is plenty of it

but nobody has decided what to do with it yet—except to re-create a room of that period. Again, its strong, square lines are masculine in the manner of Empire, and most of us associate it with our grandfathers and grandmothers. I am sure the first Eastlake room has yet to be created in Levittown or any other stronghold of modern suburbia. But just think what a conversation piece it would be if *you* did it. Why, the whole neighborhood would be a-buzzing and the next thing you knew they'd be electing you to the school board.

Jacobean, of course, is limited to side chairs. The chairs seem to fit in best with Early American pieces, and not much else. And you can use them to make a fancy little breakfast nook or in some other way in which they don't have to combine with anything.

As to Oriental (Turkish) furniture, what little can be found of it, you can't do anything with it except to use it as a joke in a rumpus room or bedroom—or large bathroom.

My friends all agreed that Mission furniture is an unqualified disaster and that the only thing you can do with it is paint it and use it on your porch. You can't give it to the junk man, because he won't take it unless you have sawed it up into lengths that will fit in his stove. It is my contention, however, that in a few years Mission will be "in," on the principle that everything gets to be "in" sooner or later, and Mission is standing next in line. I imagine the New York decorators will scrape it and bleach it and call it something like "Victorian Modern."

But Golden Oak is beginning to zoom in popularity—as anything with a marble top has done the last twenty years. The fad originated in New York City, where your eyes will pop when you see the prices those massive old round tables are going for. The interior decorators are responsible, of course. Some clean the old varnish off and revarnish to bring out the original pale-golden-yellow color. Then they make the most of the color by showing it against white walls. The ef-

fect is bright and airy—and, needless to say, very sophisticated. Others oil the wood for a richer, darker tone. An interesting place to see this sort of thing is Herb Brooks's shop,
"Discoveries," at 350 Bleecker Street in Greenwich Village.

Speaking of sophisticated, Art Nouveau is the very end of
the line in that department. You ought to be a countess—and
a rich one at that—to go in for an Art Nouveau bedroom,
which is the place it is most often used.

And now you know every single thing that I do about the
fine art of interior decorating with the various styles of Victorian furniture. And I haven't learned a thing that would
lead me to turn my back on my Eastlake band saw.

PART II

THE STYLES AND THEIR STORIES

THE POPULAR TASTE

THE FRENCH INFLUENCE

THE ENGLISH INFLUENCE

4. THE POPULAR TASTE: AN INTRODUCTION

Spool, Fancy, Cottage—the furniture that was The People's Choice.

What the three styles in this section have in common is that each in its fashion charmed the common people of their day. They existed outside the battleground of French and English Influence and the gradual triumph of the machine over hand-craftsmanship.

Neither the manufacturers nor the buyers of this furniture had ever made the Grand Tour. They had never been in the drawing rooms of the important people, the cultured people, the people who lived in the big house on the hill or the stone mansion in the city. They didn't know what was "in style," what was "good taste." All they knew was what they thought was "pretty."

The stories of the three styles, however, are quite different from one another. The fact that they are grouped together does not mean that they are related or that there is a line of development running through them. Each existed as a separate entity. Each was a staple product of merchandise that came into existence to fill a vacuum. The furniture was made because it would sell. It was created by the market. Many other styles were tried, but they died on the vine in the market place of the common man. You could call the process that took place the Darwinian Theory of Furniture Design: the survival not of the fittest but of the most popular.

The pieces discussed in this section were the "fancy" furniture of the common people, which brides pestered their husbands into buying for them so that they could "pretty up the house" a little. From the point of view of a civilization like ours, almost smothered in consumer goods, these people are hard for us to understand. But for me they were brought to life by a letter written from Chicago in 1835 and now in the Connecticut State Library in Hartford, Conn. This is a little early for the span of Cottage Furniture, but it lies at the heart of the times of Spool Furniture and the Fancy Chairs. And the same world only ten years later saw the beginnings of the Cottage Furniture.

This letter was written by Lambert Hitchcock to his partner Arba Alford. It is included here for the aura of the times that it conveys. Queen Victoria, the French, the English, Downing, and Eastlake seem very far away indeed.

Mr. Hitchcock was on a trip trying to find local agents to sell his chairs, when he wrote:

Dear Friend—

Thursday morning last I arrived in Chicago from Detroit after a journey of thirteen days, not on the most direct route to this place, but winding through the Territory from one point to another at which I wished to stop.

My first business on arrival was to go to the Office for letters. Found one from Mr. Couch, but none from you. Soon after, I requested them to look over their letters again, but none to be found, and I need not add that I felt much disappointed. Although only one month had elapsed since the time appointed for writing it, I thought still it might possibly come, and to my great satisfaction the Evening Mail, which arrives every other day from Detroit brought it. If this letter is as long in coming to you, I might as well bring it myself, for within that time

I hope to be pretty well on my way home . . . for my
own part, my health has been quite good. This is indeed
a great blessing to one eleven hundred miles from home.

The day after I wrote you from Detroit, I saddled my
poney and without company took departure for Chicago.
. . . The territory of Michigan so far as I have seen
it is remarkably level, nothing like what we in New England should call a hill is to be seen in crossing the whole
Territory . . . hence it is that the rivers and creeks are
for the most part slow, sluggish streams, one cause of
Bilious Fever and Fever and Ague. . . . The settlers
live principally in log houses, and even the Taverns and
Stage Houses are of this description except in the County
towns where generally one or more good frame Public
houses are found. These in some places answer the double
purpose of Tavern and Court-house, which with a log
jail constitute the County buildings.

Michigan, with the exception of Detroit is entirely
new. Very few inhabitants have been there more than
three years . . . hence all is new, and in a rude state.
Some with their buildings finished and a small piece of
land under cultivation are beginning to be comfortable.
Others are just into a half finished log house. Others
again have just arrived with their families on the ground
. . . where they have pitched a small tent, or sleep in
covered wagons. . . .

And now from Chicago, the London of the West as
some of the inhabitants call it, I write you. . . . The
lands in the vicinity of this village are not improved, and
nothing prevents riding in any direction over the prai-
ries.

Chicago stands on ground very level and rather low,
handsomely laid out. There are more buildings here than
I expected, but not as good. They are for the most part
cheap wood buildings. It is a place of considerable busi-

ness, and contains between four and five thousand inhabitants, has about seventy stores including groceries. There are from twenty to twenty-five lawyers, but these study speculation more than speeches. There are twelve physicians, six clergymen, and of mechanics a general assortment, among which are three chair makers. William V. Smith is here in the grocery business, and I think doing very well. And I find here also a few other acquaintances from the East. Perkins from Winsted is now in Chicago. He has been down to Jacksonville, and will probably remain in this place. . . .

And on and on Mr. Hitchcock rambled to his partner, who incidentally was also his brother-in-law. As he rambles, I can just see one of his fancy chairs being the first "imported" piece of furniture to arrive in one of those county towns. I can see a brand-new spool bed in a frame house in the village of Chicago. And then the simple painted pine furniture that we call Cottage.

The furniture that was The People's Choice.

5. SPOOL FURNITURE
1815–1880

*The most machine-oriented style of all,
it owed its life to the invention of the
multiple-bladed lathe.*

The one thing that all Victorian furniture has in common is
that it was the first furniture in history to be made by mass-
production machinery. And Spool Furniture led all the rest,
because it was made on the first machine developed for mass
production, namely, the multiple-bladed lathe, which was originally developed for making buttons and spools.

The single-blade lathe had been around for years, and that
is why some Spool Furniture comes even before the era of
furniture mass production, which we usually date as beginning with the Hitchcock and Fancy chairs in 1830.

The early Spool Furniture was made in small shops, usually on lathes that had been turning bedposts for Colonial
and Federal beds for years. But the time was ripe for innova-
tion, and some unsung genius got the idea of making his
turnings on the same kind of fast-operating, multiple-bladed
lathe that they were using in the button factory down the
road a piece.

These machines rapidly produced turnings like these:

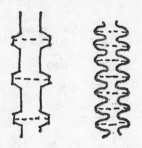

The ones on the left were cut across the grain on the dotted lines, and the resulting discs were drilled in their centers to make buttons. The ones on the right were cut and then drilled through to make spools for thread.

The application of this idea was obvious. All you needed to mass-produce Spool Furniture was a bigger multiple-bladed lathe. And so our unknown genius made one. Or maybe a lot of people got the same idea at the same time. At any rate, the idea spread quickly, and soon there were factories that made only the lengths of turning—in any size or shape wanted —for sale to the smaller cabinet shops that couldn't afford their own big lathes.

And, of course, someone eventually got the idea of splitting the turnings lengthwise and gluing them on flat surfaces as decoration, like this:

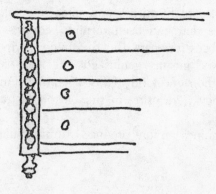

In evaluating a piece of Spool Furniture, one consideration is the quality of the wood used. For, unlike most styles of period furniture, Spool Furniture was made in almost every wood that was available. For sale to the low-priced market it was made in pine and stained to resemble mahogany. But better grades were also made of maple, cherry, whitewood (poplar), and even walnut. Of course, these were also stained to look like mahogany, the idea of light-colored furniture being a strictly modern idea. The point in using these hardwoods instead of the cheaper pine was that with them you could get a better imitation of mahogany. Sometimes mahogany *was* used, but not very often. It cost too much.

The second consideration is the earliness of the piece, and this runs fairly consistently with the degree of its simplicity. For instance, a bed with straight turnings is older than one with curved turnings. This was simply because it took a few years to invent a machine that would make curved turnings.

Furniture decorated with split lengths of turning comes at the end of the Spool Furniture period. In fact, furniture decorated in this way is usually classified as Cottage Furniture with spool decoration.

In pricing Spool Furniture there is another problem, and this one is unique. In furniture of no other style is there such a difference between the value of a piece bought in the rough and one that has been refinished. The reason is that a sad thing happens when you stain a spool turning to make it look like mahogany. The end grain of the wood is exposed on both sides of each bulb, and this porous surface soaks in the stain much more than the outer surface of the bulb does. And no known bleach or chemical can get that stain out of the end grain. It soaks in at least an eighth of an inch.

How then do we account for the lovely light-toned Spool Furniture that is often seen? The answer is that some professional cabinetmaker or refinisher has gone to the trouble of taking the piece entirely apart, has put it back in a lathe, and by holding a chisel against the spinning turning has laboriously cut an eighth of an inch off the entire surface of the piece of wood. Then, holding sandpaper against the wood as it spins, he has smoothed the surface again. Having done this to every spool, he has glued the whole piece together again and finished the wood either naturally or with a very pale stain.

That such a job should be worth around fifty dollars on the open market should not be surprising. Also it is obvious that even to tackle such a job yourself you first have to have a lathe—not exactly a common household appliance.

Don't be amazed, therefore, to find a spool bed that is covered with a couple of layers of paint going for five dollars—and then seeing the same bed priced at seventy-five dollars in an antique shop. To the five-dollar price at the auction add fifty dollars for refinishing, and you have left a profit of only twenty dollars for the dealer as his reward for recognizing the basic value of the piece, hauling it back and forth, and having his money invested in it for a year or two while it stood around his shop waiting for a buyer.

What looks at first like highway robbery turns out in this case to be a profit that is hardly worth the dealer's time and effort.

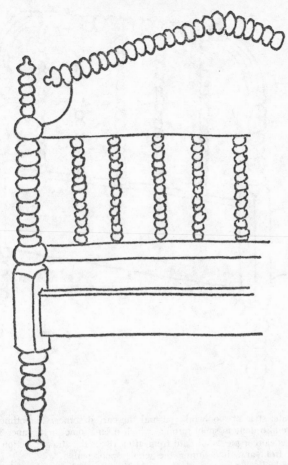

1. Throughout the whole Victorian period, the earlier things are the simplest in design and workmanship. This is plainly demonstrated by the difference between this early spool bed and the later one that follows. Notice that there are no curves. In some beds of the early kind the top was not even peaked but was made of a single stretch of horizontal spool turning. The beds were almost always made in pine and were often sold by mail order. They are often found in the company of Cottage Furniture, and the only reason for not classifying them as Cottage is that they were a specific long-lasting style, whereas most Cottage Furniture roughly reflected the current style of English or French Influence furniture that was being sold to the gentry and stylish city folk. For the current price of this bed and of all other antiques in this book, see the Price Guide that begins on page 211.

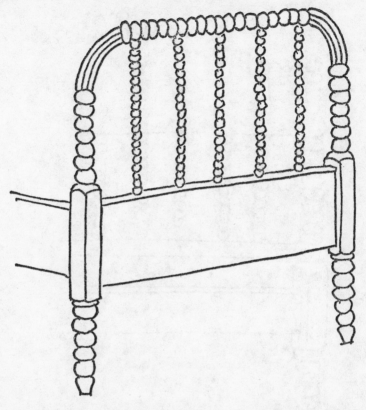

2. In this later style of spoolwork you find the curved corners. Sometimes the corners were also done in spool turning, which meant some pretty fancy lathe-work. Curved-corner pieces all date from after 1850; the straight-section style could date from any time during the whole spool period.

The later beds were also made in hardwoods, especially maple and cherry (not walnut). Most were stained and are hard to refinish, because the stain seeped deep into the end grain exposed by the turning chisels. See Price Guide entry no. 2.

3. As with the first bed shown in this section, this simple washstand would also be classed as Cottage Furniture were it not for the spool-turned legs. Pieces like this were of solid pine and were made throughout the whole period, with only minor variations in design and workmanship, and they are very hard to date. See Price Guide entry no. 3.

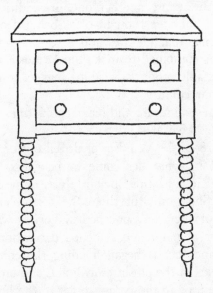

4. Small sewing and bedside tables like this one were a specialty more often made in cherry or maple than in pine. They were the treasured piece, the special wedding present, and so forth. See Price Guide entry no. 4.

6. FANCY CHAIRS
1820–1850

*Though many styles were made, the field
was dominated by Lambert Hitchcock,
the true father of mass production and
national distribution.*

Chairs are different from other pieces of furniture. They are
lighter. They are cheaper. They are movable around the house.
And you can always use another one. In addition to their
basic usefulness, they are thought of as being decorative objects—in the sense that pictures and vases and statuary are.
All these factors combined to make the Windsor chair in its
many forms a staple product of cabinetmakers from the very
beginning of our country.

Specialization soon set in, and many cabinetmakers referred
to themselves as chairmakers.

In the early 1800s the Windsor chair fell out of popularity,
to be replaced by what has come to be called the Fancy
chair. In style and line, this obviously was derived from the
side chairs of Sheraton. But there the resemblance ended.
The formality of Sheraton's polished mahogany was replaced
by bright colors of paint and stenciled decorations. And by
about 1820 Fancy chairs began flooding the country.

They were used in the plush resort hotels and on the steam-
boats that were used in those days to get to the hotels. Every
chairmaker in the country was producing his own version.
And, of course, there was Lambert Hitchcock, the father of

mass-production furniture, whose factories produced an estimated 150,000 chairs of the finest construction and durability.

I am willing to bet that three quarters of the Hitchcock chairs are still in existence. The only real threat to them was fire. And even so, if there was a chance of saving anything from a burning house, these chairs were among the easiest things to get out of a house. As to their wearing out or getting broken, I happen to know of a kitchen in Vermont where the "kitchen" chairs are original Hitchcocks. They have been used daily by one generation and another since they were demoted from the parlor just about a hundred years ago.

Hitchcock is the only Fancy chairmaker that we know anything about. This is basically because he was the only one to sign his chairs and because he sought national distribution with standard models that he stuck to over a period of years. The other manufacturers operated on a local basis and didn't strive for product and quality recognition the way Hitchcock did. (To give an idea of the size of the whole industry, it has been recorded that in the year 1825 there were 200 men in New York City alone employed in the Fancy-chair industry. They even had an early craft union, called the Master Chair Maker's Society.)

Not only can Hitchcock's chairs be identified by his "signature" on the back edge of the seats; they can also be very closely dated by the wording used. The first signature was a stenciled line of print reading: L. HITCHCOCK, HITCHCOCKSVILLE, CONNECTICUT, WARRANTED. Chairs so signed are the earliest, dating from 1822 to 1832.

In 1832 the name of the company was changed, and from 1832 to 1843 the signature read: HITCHCOCK, ALFORD & CO., WARRANTED. What happened, of course, was that Hitchcock took in a partner named Arba Alford to "tend store" while he was away on his selling trips. And he also married Mr. Alford's sister. And just to illustrate what canny Yankees these two fellows were, they decided that it would be ridiculous to build two houses next to their factory when it would be so much more economical to build one large one. But it had two front doors, and straight through the middle of it ran a solid stone wall without a single door in it. They knew a thing or two about women, too!

Anyway, the next change in the signature came in 1843, when the partners split up. Hitchcock moved to Unionville, Conn., and from 1843 to around 1850 (exact date unknown) made chairs with the signature LAMBERT HITCHCOCK, UNIONVILLE, CONNECTICUT.

Remaining at the old factory, Arba Alford took a brother into partnership and went on making chairs signed: ALFORD & COMPANY from 1843 until an uncertain date. The factory was sold about 1864 to a firm which used the machinery and other facilities for making rulers.

The decoration of Hitchcock chairs is of special interest, because it doesn't seem to stop. Many of the chairs that you see today have been "done over" and dirtied up in such a way that it is very hard to tell if the decorations are original. This is because the method used can easily be duplicated. The designs were applied by means of stencils made by tracing the designs that are on authentic chairs. Through these stencils, bronze dust of various hues was applied by the fingertip to a tacky surface beneath. Painted lines and striping were then added, and the whole covered with a protective clear coating.*

* For those who are interested in further details, the complete process is given in *The Furniture Doctor*, George Grotz, Doubleday & Company, Inc., 1962.

5. Hitchcock chairs come in many styles and backs and many a Hitchdock isn't what it seems to be. What I mean by that cynicism is that the art of forging Hitchcock stenciled designs has long been perfected, and even such gay deceivers as myself are hard put to it to tell the real thing from the fake. That goes double for the supposedly "authenticating" signature on the back of the seat. And triple for anyone who tells you he has just found a "set" of six. They were never made in sets. He has just assembled six of the same style.

The chair pictured here is the most popular style. It is called the "pillow" back, after the block of wood in the middle of the turning at the top of the back. Rush seat. (See the text for more on Hitchcock chairs.)

Never remove or paint over even traces of the original decoration unless you are also fond of lighting your pipe with dollar bills. See Price Guide entry no. 5.

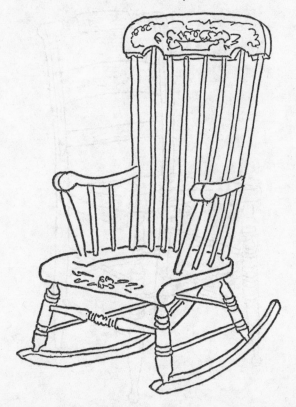

6. The so-called Boston rocker—it was made in many other places in New England—was similar to the Hitchcock chair both in the integrity of its construction and in the stenciled designs in colored bronze powders. Usually the seats were made of thick pine, the legs and arms of maple, the vertical spokes and rockers of ash, the tops of pine. There were many variations, but always the right type of wood was used for the way it had to be worked and the service it was to be put to in the chair. All the pieces were fitted together with a tightness that puts most modern furniture manufacturers to shame. See Price Guide entry no. 6.

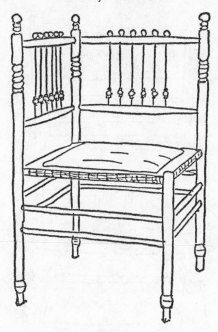

7. A Fancy chair of this kind—having no obvious relationship to any particular style—is very hard to date and may well be of a later period than the era in which Fancy chairs were so outstandingly popular. There are so many such "sports" that you could compile a book on them alone. This chair is included here as an example and to call attention to the fact that there are a great many such variations. See Price Guide entry no. 7.

8. This chair is typical of many styles of chair similar to the Hitchcock chair and made during the same time by other manufacturers—although none of them ever approached Hitchcock's tremendous volume. Decoration and construction were similar, but all the variations on the Hitchcock theme are fussier or more ornate. The chairs tended to go on river boats and into other places of amusement, whereas Hitchcock aimed for the home market. This probably accounts for there being so many more Hitchcock chairs left than of the more frivolous variety.

These fancier Fancy chairs are quite undervalued because of Hitchcock chairs having "the name" and being an established, understandable value. They are worth less than the Hitchcock chair today, but will be worth much more in the future because of their rarity. (This isn't meant to deny that Hitchcock chairs have more character and integrity of design; they hewed more closely to the line of functionalism.) See Price Guide entry no. 8.

9. Bamboo turnings were also popular in Fancy chairs and were fairly easy to think of after Spool Furniture. The wood was maple or other light-colored hardwood. The chairs were then finished with light stain or clear finish and often gilded or painted up in any fancy way that occurred. See Price Guide entry no. 9.

7. COTTAGE FURNITURE
1845–1890

*Made in tremendous volume for almost
fifty years, it filled the needs of a predomi-
nantly rural country. Made of painted
pine, it is today scraped and refinished to
provide an almost inexhaustible supply
of ersatz Early American for our antique
shops.*

Of all the styles presented in this book, Cottage Furniture
is undoubtedly the loosest classification. It doesn't derive from
any other style, and the term covers a lot of pieces that don't
look anything like each other. Even so, it is easy to identify
because all Cottage Furniture has two things in common. It
is simple of line, and (with almost no exceptions) it was
made of pine.

Cottage was the first mass-production furniture produced
for the rapidly growing middle class that the Industrial Revolution produced in this country. As such it had no artistic pre-
tensions but was made to fill a need for lots of inexpensive
furniture. Pine was cheap, light to ship, and easy to work with
the new steam-driven machinery that was rapidly replacing
the water wheels down by the old mill streams.

Now, all this sounds pretty commonplace and mercantile,
and it was. But something very interesting also happened.
Admittedly, the Cottage Furniture that preceded the Civil
War tended to have the lines of American Empire. But the

furniture produced for the mass market after the Civil War (and this was by far the greatest part of it) came closer to the ideal of functionalism in design than any other furniture in this book. The designers and promoters of the contemporary Gothic and Eastlake paid great lip service to simplicity of manufacture and to the idea that the use a piece was to be put to was the most important factor in design. They undoubtedly had good intentions, but they quickly bogged down in a morass of historic ornamentation or a sort of frantic fussiness of ornamentation for its own sake. Concerning this, see especially the section on Eastlake.

But practicality was the keynote of the Cottage Furniture made after the Civil War, and the unintended result was the beautiful simplicity of line that we find in many a dry sink, lift-top commode, and simple chest of drawers. Here you will notice a remarkable resemblance to the primitive Colonial furniture that we call Early American—which is widely reproduced even today because of its simple, functional lines.

Incidentally, this resemblance has resulted in the greatest mass of fakery in the history of furniture. For not only do these Cottage pieces have the lines of Early American, they also were made of pine. So all you have to do is strip the original paint off the piece, round the edges, take off any applied molding, beat the wood for a while with a set of rusty tire chains, stain the wood a dirty brown, and there you are. It looks like Early American and is sold as Early American. And don't try to tell anybody who owns such a piece that it isn't Early American.

Of course, if you are interested in telling the difference, the way you do it is by examining the way the piece is put together. In a fake, the hinges will be square and stubby instead of long and thin or butterfly. They will be obviously machine made instead of hammered out by a blacksmith. The dovetails on the edges of the drawers will be regular and even

—all cut at once in one swoop by a machine instead of having been hand-cut.

Incidentally, all this "Grand Rapids Pine" was originally painted and decorated, usually with false graining and pastoral scenes in the larger panels on the front of the piece. As to the problem that this presents to today's collector, see the captions that follow.

Finally, it should be pointed out that, while Spool Furniture goes way back to 1815, by 1850 it was being made of pine by the same factories that made Cottage, and was being sold along with it in the same way to the same market. The way you distinguish this "Cottage Spool" from the earlier Spool is that the Cottage Spool was made of pine, whereas the earlier Spool was made mostly of harder woods.

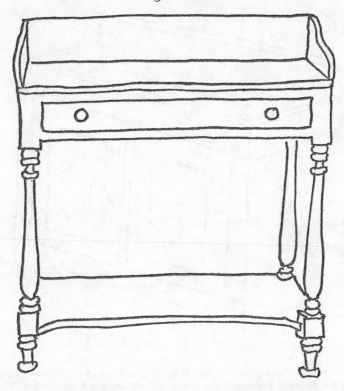

10. The commonest of the common, a painted pine washstand designed to hold pitcher and bowl on top, towels in the drawer for morning ablutions in your own bedroom. Simple in line, designed to serve a purpose rather than to imitate any style, pieces like this are an excellent example of how functionalism inevitably leads to beauty. They are still very popular because they are useful as little desks, hall tables, flower stands, and so on.

Sometimes found with pieces of poplar wood, which would indicate the piece was made in the later part of the period. See Price Guide entry no. 10.

11. A typical Connecticut dry sink. It could also be classified as Early American but certainly was made, sold, and used well into the Victorian Era. The top was used to hold a dishpan while one was washing dishes—or anything else. When found in the rough, the basin has almost always been lined with galvanized tin or even copper. When found in shops, they have invariably been refinished, with the corners rounded and the edges worn so that they can be sold as Early American. Dry sinks are very popular pieces for use as bars, serving tables, and plant stands and have already become very hard to find. See Price Guide entry no. 11.

12. The ubiquitous lift-top commode. It is even more popular than the dry sink and is happily in much greater supply because every house had more bedrooms than kitchens—as should be obvious to even the meanest intelligence. The top held a bowl and a pitcher of water, the drawer held soap and towel, and the bottom was for what we shall call here other storage.

Commodes were always sold painted, sometimes decorated with simple paneling lines, at other times false-grained and ornately decorated. Today they are found in shops scraped down and refinished in dark-stained pine and classed as Early American—which, unlike the situation with the dry sink, isn't even a possibility. However, as someone has said, it's more fun to be fooled! See Price Guide entry no. 12.

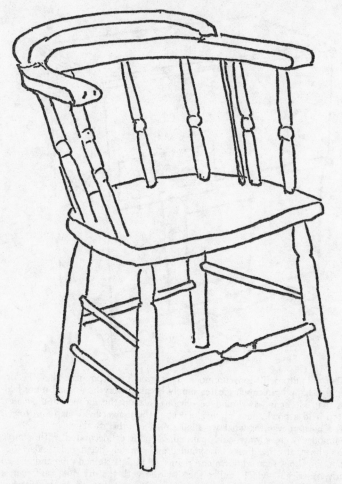

13. This is *not* a captain's chair but an office chair. The difference is that the curved back is not sawed out of pine, but bent, and usually of hickory. The rest of the sections are ordinarily of oak, but other hardwoods were also used. Mass produced, the office chair is worth far less than a real captain's chair—which was handmade and much earlier. See Price Guide entry no. 13.

14. A slightly more sophisticated washstand than the first one illustrated in this section. The hole in the top is, of course, to hold the basin. A pitcher could go on the bottom shelf, towels on the side rungs. Originally painted, now sold taken down to the natural pine. When found in shops, the top has usually been replaced with a solid piece of wood, as tables with holes in their tops aren't very useful these days. See Price Guide entry no. 14.

15. When is a chair a Fancy chair, and when is it a piece of Cottage
Furniture—especially when Fancy chairs were sold at the same time to the
same people who bought Cottage Furniture? Anyway, odd chairs like these—
and their variations are legion—are made of all kinds of wood, but mostly
maple. See Price Guide entry no. 15.

16. Shades of the Shakers! When you get completely utilitarian about making a chest of drawers, this is what you come up with. While this drawing may be no beauty, a piece like this finished in the natural pine, stained to bring out the grain, is a lovely, simple little thing. See Price Guide entry no. 16.

17. A common and useful little table of pine. See the similar one and notes about it in the section on Spool Furniture. See Price Guide entry no. 17.

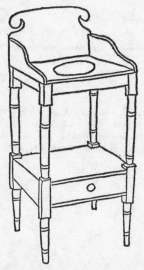

18. Here we have a washstand similar to the one illustrated on page 49. It is included because it is a piece of Cottage Furniture strongly derivative from one of the "higher" styles—namely, Empire. To see this clearly, compare this piece with the washstand pictured in the section on Empire. While the Empire piece was made of fine figured mahogany and finished naturally, this one was made of pine and painted. The two pieces that follow are derivative of Empire, a fact that establishes these pieces as quite early in the Cottage Furniture era. See Price Guide entry no. 18.

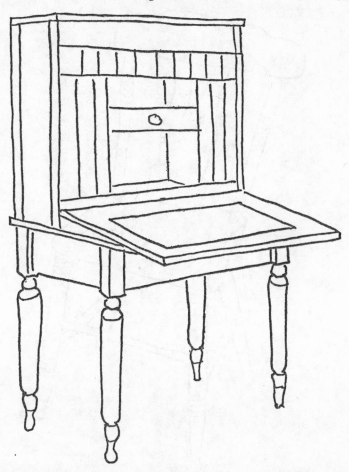

19. Continuing the remarks in the previous caption, the derivation of this table desk from the Empire style can be seen by glancing through the illustrations in that section of the book. The writing surface folds up and locks. The top is removable for easier transportation, but the piece was originally made as one unit and is not a mongrel. Desks of this kind were often owned by schoolmasters, who took them with them when they moved to another school. The wood was pine or cherry or a combination. Oak in later versions. See Price Guide entry no. 19.

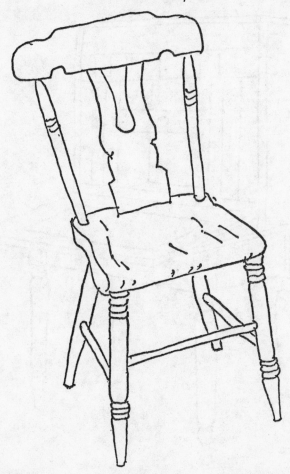

20. While this chair isn't particularly appealing to me, it is included here because it is another example of early Cottage Furniture derivative of the Empire style, the first of our imported styles and so widely popular that it is more American than French. For this reason it is sometimes called American Empire. See preceding two captions.

This chair had a pine seat and back, and maple legs. See Price Guide entry no. 20.

21. The settee or bench has always been a popular piece, and this is a very early one (perhaps even before 1845) of pine seat and back, maple arms, and ash spokes. Many different kinds of wood were used. See Price Guide entry no. 21.

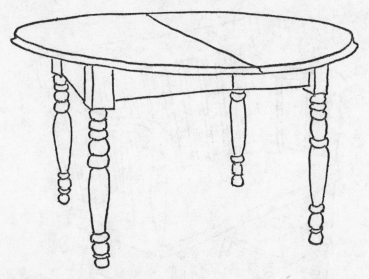

22. Millions of these fine old pine tables must have been made—and a lot in cherry, too, which was stained and sold as mahogany. Later they were made in oak. The wood used establishes their value. See Price Guide entry no. 22.

23. Speaking of derivative Cottage Furniture (see pages 52, 53, and 54), here we have two pieces—this and the one that follows—which are obviously low-priced versions of the Renaissance style. The essential difference is that these are made of pine and are painted instead of being of naturally finished walnut.

For years it has been common practice to scrape such pieces down and sell them as Early American Pine—without the backboards. (A patch strip along the back of the top is the tip-off.) But as every day goes by, this becomes a more frightful thing to do, even from an economic point of view. Not to mention ranking yourself with the Goths and Vandals in regard to the artifacts of the beginnings of our American culture. Especially if the false graining and/or decoration is in good condition.

However, small commodes like these are still being sold as "in the rough" and then scraped down and sold as ersatz Early American Pine—except in the more sophisticated cities. See Price Guide entry no. 23.

24. See previous caption, which also applies to this commode. See also Price Guide entry no. 24 for further details.

8. THE FRENCH INFLUENCE: AN INTRODUCTION

The last of the designs oriented to traditional handcraftsmanship.

To understand American furniture of French influence, we must remember the world for which it was made. In the early 1800s, the population of this country was only thirteen million, and 90 per cent of them existed along a narrow strip of the Atlantic seaboard. All roads were dirt roads, and travel was rare—except among the very wealthy. Even then it was only for men of great affairs, who traveled because they had to.

Water came out of wells, not faucets. Heat came out of fireplaces, not radiators. Every furrow turned was turned by a single plow. Practically everybody had to work ten hours a day, six days a week, just to keep alive. An incredible 85 per cent of our people were involved either in agriculture or in the distribution of food. The steamboat hadn't arrived on the scene. The cotton gin and the power-driven looms of New England were still to come. Clothes were handmade and so was the cloth. Broadcloth. A man didn't buy a suit a year: he bought one for life.

And furniture? Two or three pieces and some sheets were considered a respectable dowry. There was no such thing as a furniture store. Not a single one. Most people got their furniture by inheriting a few pieces and making a few more. Of course, the bigger towns had their own cabinetmakers.

In this era, furniture of French influence was the furniture of the rich, the landed gentry, the whaling captains and their backers. But this era was also one of great growth, and the numbers of those who could afford to buy furniture expanded rapidly up to the Civil War. The rising middle class bought furniture in styles already accepted by their longer-established betters. Mostly they bought Empire, which came in with Napoleon and the French Revolution.

9. EMPIRE
1810–1840

The first attempt to reject nonintegral ornamentation.

Empire originated in France as a reaction to the effeminate, overdecorated styles of the decadent French aristocracy. To the French, it expressed a contrasting strength and stability. It was to be the furniture of the new world they had created through revolution. And we, their brothers in recent revolution and thinking, went right along with that idea. Except that, after the first few years, the French couldn't resist putting some decorations and curlicues on these simple, massive pieces. Our puritan background seems to have helped us to resist this, and as time goes by, our American version of Empire looks more and more modern.

At first this furniture was made of solid mahogany, but the increasing demand for it—as more people could buy it—soon led the cabinetmakers to use mahogany veneer over pine wherever possible. The later pieces were entirely of this kind. Over the last fifty years, incidentally, many Empire pieces have been thrown into lakes, where, after about a week, the veneer peels off easily—and *voilà!* you have an Early American pine chest. Not really, because the massive, heavy lines still are there to the knowing eye. But then, a lot of eyes aren't knowing.

As to the lines of the furniture, we find the French basically under the domination of Greece and Rome. Empire may have been born of a reaction, but it still doesn't introduce any fundamentally new idea—and none of the French or English furniture of the preceding century did so either. If that sounds like another dig against the so-called Golden Age of Furniture Design, so cherished by the expensive galleries and certain slick-paper magazines, that's exactly what it is supposed to be. Isn't it about time that somebody pointed out that the Emperor doesn't really have any clothes on?

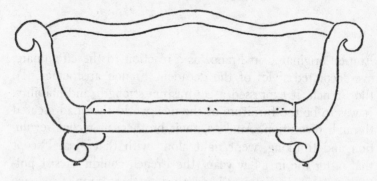

25. The ponderous but gracefully curved sections of this typical Empire couch were cut out of great blocks of pine over which were glued plain and figured mahogany veneers. This applies to the legs, arms, and even the curved stretcher at the top of the back. They were popular pieces for many years. See Price Guide entry no. 25.

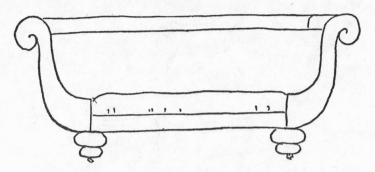

26. There are fewer of these couches with the straight back, and collectors value them higher than the type immediately preceding. The legs may be of the bulbous type shown here, common in the Empire style, or of the type in the preceding illustration. Woods used and construction are also the same as that in the preceding piece. See Price Guide entry no. 26.

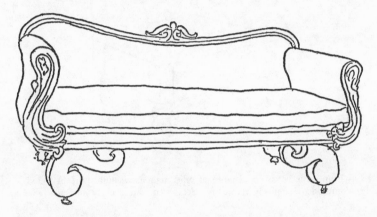

27. Here we see the beginnings of the Baroque style being grafted onto the basic Empire couch. Construction is the same. The difference is simply in the ornate hand-carving, which was glued on. See Price Guide entry no. 27.

28. A beautifully constructed piece of solid mahogany, quite pure in the style, this commode was nicely refinished. See Price Guide entry no. 28.

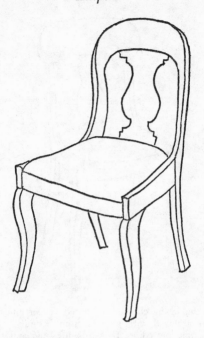

29. A typical chair of the period, pure in style. The curved back is mahogany, with figured mahogany veneer glued on the face. All other parts are mahogany. See Price Guide entry no. 29.

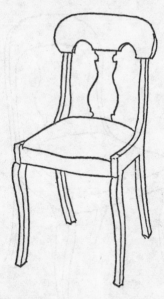

30. Another solid mahogany chair with figured veneer glued on the face of the back, which is attached with screws (from behind). Quite typical. In this chair and the one preceding, the seats lift out, making them easy to re-cover. See Price Guide entry no. 30.

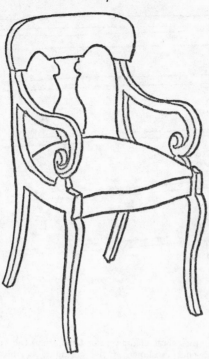

31. The armchair variation for the head of the table. Matches the chair shown in the preceding illustration. Same lift-out seat. See Price Guide entry no. 31.

32. The typical Empire chest of drawers or bureau had the same massive but graceful air as the couches shown at the beginning of this section. It was constructed of great chunks of pine covered over with plain and figured mahogany veneers. This was even true of the drawers, including the knobless one at the top. The only solid mahogany piece was the top. See Price Guide entry no. 32.

33. Some Empire melodeons were considerably more massive than this portable model, but there weren't many of them, and this piece was very popular. They were made with gradual changes in style all the way to the end of the Renaissance period. They were operated with a bellows forcing air through the reeds—as opposed to the pipes in an organ. See Price Guide entry no. 33.

34. This early Empire secretary has simple lines and was made of solid mahogany rather than the veneered, coated pine used for the more massive pieces. Such pieces are cherished by serious collectors. See Price Guide entry no. 34.

35. Some early chests of drawers were also made of solid mahogany before massive variation on the style became popular. A small chest like this can be a very charming piece. See Price Guide entry no. 35.

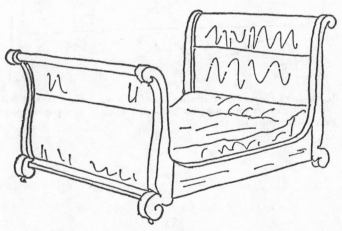

36. The famous sleigh bed was so named because it looked like one of the horse-drawn variety. Its construction was of pine, covered with mahogany veneer, although thin sheets of solid mahogany were used in the head- and footboards. See Price Guide entry no. 36.

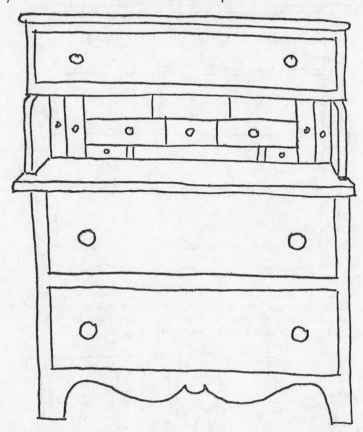

37. Resembling a chest of drawers when closed, this was really a butler's desk, used by said butler for organizing his bills and records. A very popular piece. See Price Guide entry no. 37.

38. A more straightforward desk or small secretary on pure Empire lines. The working surface slides in, as do the supports under it. Usually all solid mahogany, with the exception of the drawer fronts, which were pine covered with mahogany veneer. An early and valuable piece. See Price Guide entry no. 38.

39. A small pedestal table in the Empire style. See Price Guide entry no. 39.

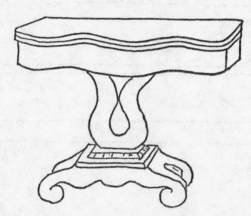

40. One of the most attractive, distinctive, and popular of the Empire pieces is the lyre table, of which a great many were made. The top opens up, twists around for better support by the base, and makes a fine card table. Solid mahogany top, veneer-covered pine for the lyre and base. See Price Guide entry no. 40.

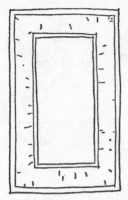

41. The famous ogee mirror that must have been made by the millions. Made of pine covered with figured mahogany veneer, most of these have been ruined by dealers who soak the veneer off in a tub or lake, then sell them as Early American Pine. See Price Guide entry no. 41.

42. The marble-top commode in solid mahogany is quite early and is very good-looking. See Price Guide entry no. 42.

10. LOUIS XV
1830–1860

The finger molding and curves that later
would so outrage Mr. Eastlake.

Overlapping and following Empire, we come to Louis XV, which until recently has been considered most typically Victorian. This furniture was by far the most popular from its introduction until the tremendous industrial expansion in this country due to the Civil War. Far more of it was made and sold than of the other two styles that we list under French Influence—Baroque and Belter.

In respect to design, we find the American to be a much simplified version of its mother style in France. But by now our sleepy agricultural country had started to bustle, with the opening up of our waterways, the coming of the railroads, expansion to the Midwest, and the beginning of mass-production factories. We were rapidly becoming sophisticated, and our ladies wanted something more interesting, more ornate in their parlors. And as everyone knows, what the ladies want, the ladies get. This was the era of plush carpets, miles of hanging draperies, the gold rush, and the girl in the gilded cage.

Louis XV, then, marked a movement away from starkness and simplicity. The basic wood was black walnut, however, because there wasn't enough mahogany to go around. Of course, mahogany was still considered more desirable and some pieces were made of it. Also some fancy pieces were made of rosewood.

This furniture cannot yet be considered to be really mass-produced—but almost. Cabinet shops had expanded to the point where one man made legs all day, another arms, and so forth. For instance, Duncan Phyfe had to turn to making this kind of furniture to stay in business (until 1846) and his shop was known to employ as many as a hundred men at a time.

The basic characteristics of Louis XV are, of course, the curves, the so-called finger molding, and the decoration with leaves or bunches of grapes. (The decoration was to be carried over, as we will see in the next section, to furniture of the English Influence.)

Louis XV still was put together with dowels—as opposed to the machine-cut slotted joints that were to follow. Slotted joints had, in fact, started with the mass-production furniture that was already being made for the new English-dominated taste of the masses, Gothic and Renaissance.

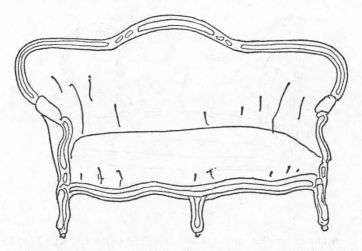

43. When we look at a piece like this, it is hard to agree with Eastlake, Morris, Stickley, etc., that curves in furniture were really so unforgivable. Poor use was made of the material (in this case mahogany), which is a lot stronger in straight sections, but anyone who thinks that a Louis XV sofa isn't a thing of beauty is a hard case, indeed. See Price Guide entry no. 43.

44. The medallion-back sofa is a frequent variation of the preceding piece, and the same comments apply. Again mahogany was the wood used, and these pieces invariably have to be completely reglued and reupholstered before they can be used—and even then, they don't belong in any rumpus room. See Price Guide entry no. 44.

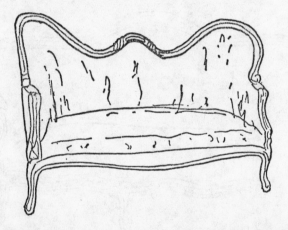

45. A further variation on the theme established in the two preceding illustrations. Finger-molding carving—all done by hand—is found in all these pieces. The wood is invariably mahogany. The glue was hide glue or fish glue —similar to mucilage—the most unfortunate invention in the history of furniture, because it softens in damp weather, and all the furniture of this era has to be reglued. See Price Guide entry no. 45.

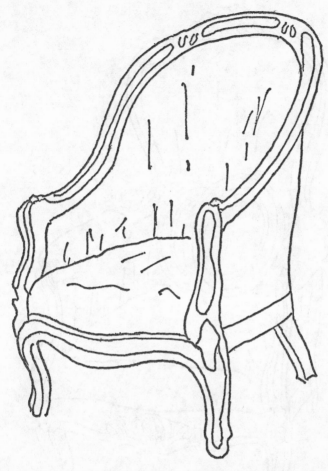

46. Here we have what has recently come to be called a Sleepy Hollow chair. It originated in this period as a distinct, new piece of furniture, and was picked up by the designers of the English Influence. (See illustration on page 114, in the section on Eastlake.) A heavier, more compact frame makes it a lot safer to lounge in than most pieces of this style. See Price Guide entry no. 46.

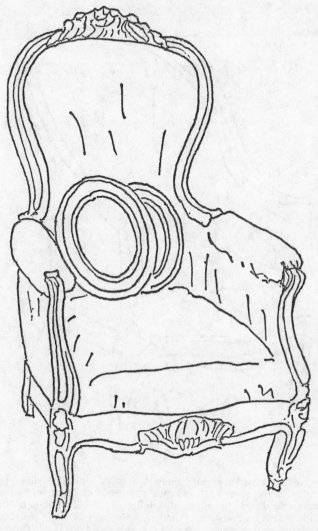

47. A lady's chair, with mirrors. The chair is similar to the preceding, which
was the corresponding gentleman's chair. See Price Guide entry no. 47.

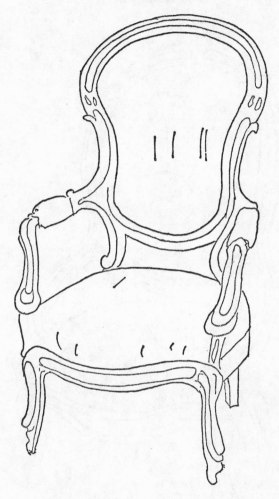

48. Another variation of the two preceding chairs, but heavy and gross by comparison. Probably made at the end of the period. See Price Guide entry no. 48.

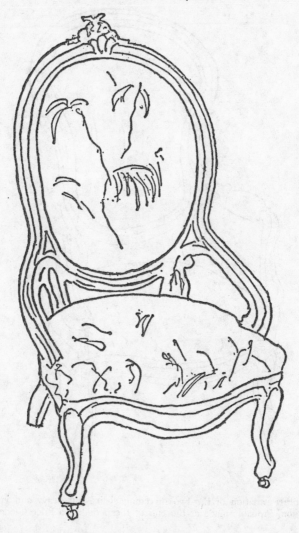

49. Somewhat more feminine than the preceding chair, this one is also late in the period. See Price Guide entry no. 49.

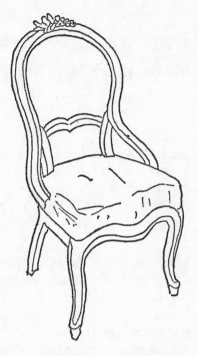

50. A classic chair of the period. Sometimes the back was upholstered. See Price Guide entry no. 50.

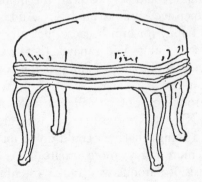

51. Footstools were very popular during the era, and ones like this are still highly valued today. See Price Guide entry no. 51.

11. BAROQUE, WHICH INCLUDES THE REMARKABLE MR. BELTER
1835–1870

Also called Rococo, it was the culmina-
tion of the wood-carver's art or craft. In
Belter, an inventive German went even
further than anyone thought possible.

During approximately the same years that the Louis XV style was popular, a good deal of furniture derived from it was being made along much more ornate lines. There is always someone who wants to go a little further than the people next door. This was Baroque, the furniture of the rich, back in the grand old days when it wasn't considered bad taste to be ostentatious, but just a lot of fun. Those were the days when a millionaire could say, "See all the money I've made. See all the expensive stuff I can buy." And in those days everybody was happy for him because they all expected to be able to do the same thing. Well, maybe there were exceptions. Like the twelve-year-old kids working in the coal mines—but who could hear them?

Anyway, Baroque cannot be called a style or even a sub-style of Louis XV. It is more like a classification. Under it fall all the wild things that you could do to make Louis XV more flowery, more curvy, more ornate.

Since the basis of Baroque was frankly ostentation, it is not surprising to find that it was mostly made for parlor sets. The biggest producer was an immigrant from Germany, John Henry Belter.

Belter's fame rests partly on the fact that all his pieces are identifiable. If you own a Belter piece, there is no question about it, and you can be just as ostentatious about it as if you owned a piece of real Chippendale. In fact, it is always possible that the Chippendale is a fake—but never a Belter. This typically German character invented a mechanical process by which he could go further than anybody else in ornateness. Long before anyone had heard of plywood, he was making it in six to eight layers of very thin rosewood. This could be carved and "pierced" to a degree that no solid wood could be without losing its structural strength. He even molded his laminated wood in curved sections by means of large presses. But all the carving and assembling was still done by hand.

Belter took himself very seriously. Before he died he went down to his shop one gloomy afternoon and busted and burned all the patterns and molds used in fabricating his designs to prevent anyone else from using them after his death —thus preserving the integrity of the pieces he had made.

Of course, Belter's pieces were only a drop in the bucket of Baroque furniture, and the wild variety of pieces produced for this "ostentation market" has done much to confuse the issue respecting the fundamental Victorian styles. Many pieces made in this period just aren't of any style, and you can't see the trees for the forest. This is why it is useful to call them a "class" of furniture, placing them all under the classification of Baroque.

The same sort of obfuscation will occur again when we reach the end of the Eastlake chapter of our story. But with the next step things clear up considerably with the arrival on the scene of a young architect named Andrew Jackson Downing. With him, we start the story of the styles of English Influence and the real beginning of machine production of furniture.

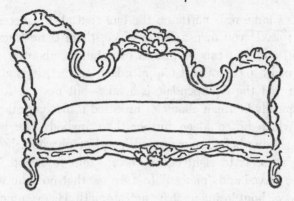

52. Pieces like this couch were made of solid mahogany that was ornately hand-carved. The workmanship was of a very high quality throughout. There are very few such pieces around, because not many were made. They were the furniture of the rich. Because of their rarity and the integrity of their construction, they are valued high. See Price Guide entry no. 52.

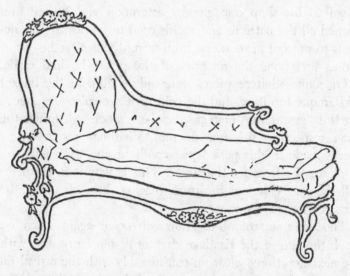

53. Though this piece doesn't look anything like the previous one (except for the foliage) it comes from the same era and illustrates the fact that all that Baroque means in terms of American Victorian furniture is fanciness, a degenerate ostentation based on Louis XV. See Price Guide entry no. 53.

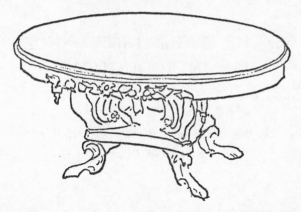

54. The ornate tables of this era also developed along no particular lines except that they stemmed from Louis XV. Hard to find. Always solid mahogany. See Price Guide entry no. 54.

55. The aristocrat of Victorian. You will rarely see Belter in an antique shop. Whenever pieces turn up, the dealers take them straight to collectors. See text for further description. See Price Guide entry no. 55.

12. THE ENGLISH INFLUENCE: AN INTRODUCTION

*Rooted in the past, it showed stirrings of
Modern.*

The English-style furniture in the following pages is far more typically Victorian than is the Louis XV style. And of the English styles, the Eastlake-Morris would be the most outstandingly Victorian.

Through the major styles of this period—Gothic, Renaissance, Eastlake-Morris, Mission, Golden Oak—we can trace the emergence of modern furniture design. Although the first two of these styles carry names that would suggest strong roots in the past, furniture was now being made by machinery and had to be designed with that fact in mind.

Throughout the whole period recurred the claim that each style was more *functional* than the last. From our modern viewpoint, some of the things from Downing on don't look very functional at all, but the furniture makers all meant the same thing that we do by the word today: The better a piece of furniture serves the purpose for which it was intended the more beautiful, the more pleasing to the eye, and the more satisfactory to the spirit it will be.

Whether you agree with this or not, and whether modern furniture is all it is supposed to be or not, the idea resulted in the first "new look" in furniture since the days of the Greeks and Romans. This was not the case with Gothic and Renaissance (though people thought it did at the time), but it is obvious in Eastlake-Morris, Mission, Golden Oak, and of course Modern.

To design for manufacture by machine is one thing. To design for beauty through functionalism is another. But the two approaches are in no conflict at all. Also they came from the same background: industrialism as a new world of our own making. If we threw off the shackles of the past, we could make anything we wanted to, better than it had ever been made in the past. For that was the spirit in the hearts of men in the Victorian Era, and the two approaches to design were happily wedded.

13. GOTHIC
1840–1870

The amazing one-man revolution by an architect named Andrew Jackson Downing.

At first glance, a switch in taste from French forms to Gothic ones may not seem very revolutionary—just a random casting about for something new and different. But this change was actually very meaningful and exciting at the time, because of the way the people felt about it.

To tell the story, we must first point out that nobody sat down and thought up Gothic Furniture. It was an inevitable by-product. What someone sat down and thought up—almost out of a clear blue sky—was Gothic architecture. And Gothic Furniture was made simply to match and fill the houses built in this style during the twenty-five years preceding the Civil War.

The man responsible for Gothic Furniture is the man who "thought up" Gothic architecture. He was an amazing young man named Andrew Jackson Downing, who grew up among the splendid estates that lined the Hudson River near Newburgh, New York.

He started life humbly enough as one of five children of a gardener who started his own nursery to supply shrubs and plants for the estates of the area. But young Andrew was a good student—at first of horticulture, then landscape architecture—and was taken up by the cultured, widely traveled people who lived in the great mansions. He learned fast, so fast that by the time he got married at twenty-five he had already developed some strong ideas about the kind of houses people should live in.

To begin with, he rejected the idea that a house should look like a Greek temple. (In the preceding years Greek Revival had been the most popular style of house to fill up with French-looking furniture.) He thought that a house should serve the purpose for which it was built—namely, to serve the people who lived in it. Lo! The idea of functionalism struck root in our soil.

Now, of course, you will say, "But houses that look like Gothic castles? That's more functional than houses that look like Greek temples? What's the difference?" There was a difference. The house that Downing built for his bride was a lot more functional inside and a lot more practical to build and maintain outside. After all, you must judge a man's achievement in relation to the times in which he lived. If we think having a house look like a Gothic house is pretty funny, it was a step toward reason after all, and the fellow who takes the first step deserves credit, no matter how small the step.

Gothic Furniture, like the Gothic house in architecture, was more practical, more useful, more lasting, and better designed for the purpose it was to serve than was the furniture of the French Influence. French furniture was quickly pushed aside as Downing's ideas swept the country. Coincidentally, the growing furniture industry picked up the new designs with relish, because their straight lines made them much easier to produce with early woodmaking machinery than were the curvy French styles.

And so the circular saws, planing machines, automatic routers, and molding cutters tore into the planks of black walnut, occasionally mahogany, and even some rosewood.

56. A Gothic secretary comes so early in the Victorian furniture of the English Influence that it doesn't really have the flavor of the rest of the new antiques. It was more slavishly copied from a European style and is more of a parent to the styles to follow. It was certainly one of the finest pieces of furniture made in the Victorian Era, containing a great deal of fine handwork and careful construction. The wood was the finest native walnut. See Price Guide entry no. 56.

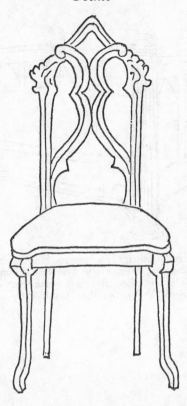

57. Gothic chairs are also quite rare. This one is of carved walnut. See Price Guide entry no. 57.

58. A bed like this really belongs in a museum, and that is probably the only place you would find one, because few were made. Fundamentally, it was made to furnish Gothic mansions, and there weren't very many of those outside the Hudson River Valley. See Price Guide entry no. 58.

14. RENAISSANCE
1850–1885

In the era of Lord Byron and the Brownings, the British discovered the Italian Renaissance, and romanticism set the idea of functionalism back—but not for long.

A Lincoln rocker can hardly be classed as being in the Renaissance style, but Renaissance Furniture can well be thought of as the furniture of Lincoln's times, spanning the years the Civil War. Lincoln may not have rocked in Renaissance, but when he wandered into Mary's parlor he was surrounded by it and had to weave his way through it.

The Renaissance style also represents the taste of a country that was booming, in spite of the bloody Civil War. "Something fancier" was wanted than the austerity of Downing's grim Gothic lines, and concurrent with the change of taste was the development of more complicated machinery—the band saw and carving machine, for example—for mass producing furniture with curves and carvings. Of course, whether the machines or the furniture came first is like asking which came first, the chicken or the egg. And to neither problem do I propose an answer.

Renaissance furniture is supposedly derived from the Italian Renaissance of Michelangelo and the Sistine Chapel, Titian's red-headed women, and all that luxurious sort of thing. How, then, can we say it is furniture of the "English Influence"?

The answer, of course, is that we picked up our interest secondhand from the English, who were at about that time discovering the sunny shores of Italy and the remains of Renaissance times. There was Dante Gabriel Rossetti. There was that fellow Byron, who even went and fought with Garibaldi in the Italian revolution that corresponded to our own revolution and that of the French. And, of course, there was Robert Browning, who finally managed to get his Elizabeth away from the rest of the Barretts of Wimpole Street. And you know where they went to write her sonnets and things.

The basic wood used for Renaissance was still black walnut. But fancy burl veneer was often glued onto the little decorative shields or panels. Rosewood was sometimes used, and in the cheaper grades even pine, stained to resemble mahogany or rosewood.

This fakery was done by dipping a shaggy sponge into black ink and dragging it over the surface of the pine to leave irregular streaks and a few swirls. Then the whole piece was dyed a dark red and finally coated with a brownish shellac or lacquer. The process was widely used on Cottage Furniture and all kinds of Fancy chairs as well. The swirling black marks have caused more grief to antique dealers and amateur refinishers than anything since women were given the vote.

The grief, of course, comes from the fact that there is no way known either to old-timers or to modern science of getting the black streaks out of the wood. The reason, I am told by a couple of Ph.D.s at New Haven, is that the black isn't a dye but carbon, whose fine particles have been carried by some solvent deep into the grain of the wood. And carbon, it seems, is something that is black and stays black.

So, if you remove the finish from something and find these streaks, give up. Right away. All you can do is either (1) refinish the piece with red stain and brown shellac the way it was originally done, or (2) paint it flat black or gold and decorate it.

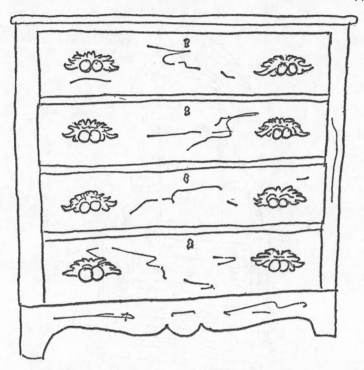

59. This chest has the typical carved-walnut handles of fruit-and-leaf design. In this case, plums instead of the usual grapes. Or maybe they are just big grapes. This piece was a lower-priced version in solid walnut with a walnut top.

Variation: Very similar pieces—but with a straight line at the base—were made in solid walnut with marble tops. See Price Guide entry no. 59.

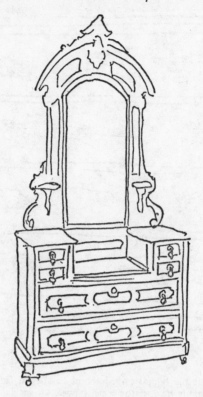

60. Here we have a fancier and somewhat later version of the preceding chest. These bureaus were always (almost always, anyhow) made of solid walnut, with fancily figured veneer in the panels. The teardrop pulls were ordinarily used, but carved leaves or carved leaves and grapes are common. The small shelves on either side of the mirror were used for candles. Usually the mirrors tilt forward and back so that you can get a better view of your hemline. The three tops were of white marble. Not many of these are in the shops yet because of their size, and then only in the most sophisticated areas.

Variation: Much cheaper versions of this piece were sometimes made in pine. They were false-grain with paint and had rural-type decorations on the drawer fronts (sheaves of wheat, for instance). They were for sale to country folk, a lot of them going through mail-order catalogues. They will be worth more than their walnut counterparts when people start appreciating them (because by then they will be very rare). See Price Guide entry no. 6o.

61. A whatnot or set of shelves to stick in a corner and fill with gewgaws. In this style they were made in solid walnut.

It is doubtful that any of these were made in pine during this period. A few in mahogany, however—which would have about the same valuation as those in walnut. See Price Guide entry no. 61.

62. This chest was built of solid walnut, with walnut moldings glued on. The corner columns are derivative of Empire. Carved wooden handles. Almost always there is a marble top. A standard or classic piece, typical of the style. See Price Guide entry no. 62.

63. Speaking of pieces being derivative of Empire, this commode is a real problem to classify. It is Empire in general line. The difference is in the grape-and-leaf pull, the curves of the marble top, and the fact that it is made of walnut instead of mahogany. See Price Guide entry no. 63.

64. Here we have a Renaissance headboard of the later period. It came under the general influence of Eastlake's ideas, mainly in the design of the decorative paneling at the top. The beds are enormous and of solid walnut. They are hardly ever found in antique shops because they take up so much space and sell so slowly. And junk shops and auctions are about the only sources. Sometimes at auctions no one will bid anything on them because there is no way to carry them and nobody has a room big enough to hold one. Sometimes they are over eight feet high. Beautiful pieces, but definitely white elephants. See Price Guide entry no. 64.

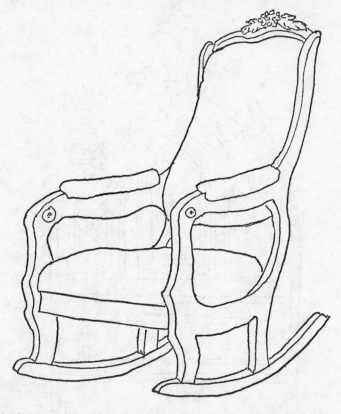

65. While walnut was definitely the wood of this period, rockers like these were often made in mahogany. See Price Guide entry no. 65.

66. A large whatnot with mirror and sometimes umbrella stands was called an *étagère* and used in the hallway of a typical Victorian house. It is what you call a decorator piece, and is usually painted white and antiqued with a brown glaze. See Price Guide entry no. 66.

67. A classic little marble-top commode derivative of Empire. Sometimes found with teardrop pulls. See Price Guide entry no. 67.

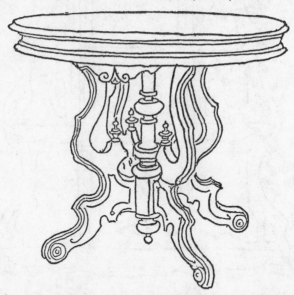

68. Shades of *Gone With the Wind*, Mrs. Lincoln's parlor, and the birds in the Silver Cages of the Silver Barons! Solid walnut and beautiful workmanship are used in this marble-top table, which is the most popular piece of all Victorian furniture. Even a young fellow like me remembers when you could get them for $5 or $10, because nobody wanted them. Then they began going as cocktail tables if you cut the tops of the legs off so that they were only about 19 inches high. But by now that would be considered a sacrilege. See Price Guide entry no. 68.

69. This considerably simpler version of the preceding table was made of walnut but didn't have a marble top. Probably made for the mail-order trade. See Price Guide entry no. 69.

70. Originally the spool cabinet was used in the dry-goods stores of the time and carried advertising on the drawer panels. Of solid walnut with turned walnut pulls, it is a fascinating piece to almost everyone. See Price Guide entry no. 70.

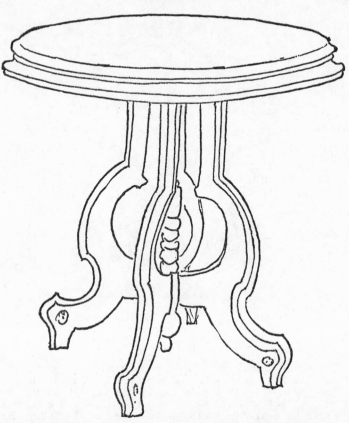

71. Another typical small marble-top table of a less-ornate style than the first one shown in this section. See Price Guide entry no. 71.

72. With a chair like this you run into the real problem of separating the Victorian styles. It was made at the end of the period, and the influence of Eastlake is very strong—in the knobs and style of the paneling across the top. And yet it still looks a lot like the bed shown on page 101. The top of a similar chair that I show here has crossed the line and would definitely have to be called Eastlake. The people who made furniture in those days were out to capture the public fancy of the moment and didn't care about all the trouble they were going to put collectors to in later years. See Price Guide entry no. 72.

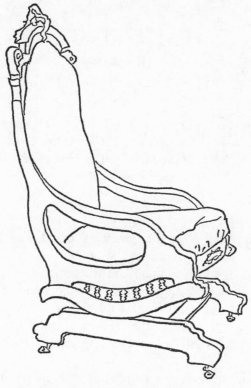

73. Platform rocker. See Price Guide entry no. 73.

15. EASTLAKE
1870–1890

*The man who hated curves. His ideas
swept the country, but his victories were
stolen from him by the men with the
carving machines.*

After the Civil War the country boomed, and Renaissance
furniture was mass-produced with growing ornateness. The
time was ripe for reaction. And reaction came. It came with
a bang. It came with the arrival on the scene of a reformer
who was to become the most misunderstood, misinterpreted,
and maligned man in the history of furniture design—Sir
Charles Lock Eastlake, an English painter, architect, and art
critic.

The idea really began with the English philosopher William
Morris, who had been for some years urging a return to hand-
crafts as a reaction against the increasing mechanization of
the Industrial Revolution and its dehumanization of man in
his daily life. But Eastlake carried this idea more directly into
the field of furniture by writing a book called *Hints on Household Taste in Furniture, Upholstery and Other Details*,
published in England in 1868 and in the United States in
1872.

In both countries the influence of this book was immediate and enormous. The best explanation for this effect is
given by Russell Lynes in his book *The Tastemakers*. Eastlake's new designs, he wrote, "not only had the fascination
of a new look, but . . . the arguments that went with them

had the ring of high moral purpose and high aesthetic deals. Here was a chance not only to redecorate but to be saved at the same time." In other words, it gave our grandparents a chance to bring the spirit of their revival meetings right into their own homes.

What were the designs that all this fuss was about? The answer can best be told in Eastlake's own words. Here is what he thought of Renaissance, the "Modern" furniture of the day:

> Our modern sofas and chairs aspire to elegance . . . simply because there is not a straight line in their composition. . . . The tendency of the present age runs exclusively to curves. A curve in the back of a sofa is manifestly inconvenient, for it is either too high in one place or too low in another to accommodate the shoulders of a sitter. Chairs are curved to insure the greatest amount of ugliness and the least amount of comfort. The legs of cabinets are curved in a senseless manner and become constructively weak. Tables curved in every direction horizontally and vertically are inconvenient to sit at. . . .
>
> This detestable system of ornamentation is called 'shaping.' It always involves additional expense in manufacture, and the product is not structurally sound. . . .
>
> The subject of carved wood is an equally important question, because nothing but a vigorous and radical reform will help us on this point. It may be layed down as a general rule that whenever wood carving is introduced into the design of modern furniture, it is egregiously and utterly bad. It is frequently employed in the most inappropriate places, is generally spiritless in design, and always worthless in execution. A great deal of this work is actually done by machine and there are shops where enriched wood moulding and scroll work can be purchased by the yard. . . . Even if it were carved out of wood, it

would be objectionable; but most of this trash is glued on articles of furniture which by their own elaborate nature cannot stand any further embellishment.

Now there was a fellow who wasn't afraid to say what he thought. And everybody was so stunned that they immediately decided he was right. And though the word was still to come into use, what Eastlake advocated, of course, was the same "functionalism" that Downing was after with his Gothic designs.

What actually happened was a different matter. In the beginning a little of Eastlake's square, solid, practical furniture was made. But two factors conspired to defeat his lofty aims.

The first was that all the newly built furniture factories had tools for cutting curves and carving moldings. In the competitive market they naturally used them, each manufacturer trying to make his furniture look a little different from the other fellow's.

The second factor was that a tremendous cultural event occurred in the year 1876—the Centennial Exposition in Philadelphia. For the first time the cultural leaders of our society were exposed en masse to what was happening in art and interior decoration in Europe—notably England, France, and Germany. In those countries too, it seems, machines for manufacturing ornateness had run rampant, in hundreds of ways that Americans had never thought of. Like hungry trout we jumped at the bait: the fundamental shapes of Eastlake's square furniture persisted, but it was quickly covered over with patterns and design motifs that defy classification. The era of bric-a-brac fretwork was at hand and it flourished wildly on the corpse of Eastlake's solid oaken boxes.

The next forward step in the cause of simplicity and "functional" design was not to come until almost the turn of the century. But before we look at that event, we should examine two oddities running parallel to the defeat of Eastlake's style.

74. If it is Eastlake we are going to have, let us start out with the most Eastlake that we can find. And here is a masterpiece of the genre, a stand-up-to-it desk, or secretary if you choose. The basic construction is oak, with burl walnut veneer on the raised paneling. See Price Guide entry no. 74.

75. A popular piece already, especially in the Middle West, this is the Eastlake version of the Sleepy Hollow chair in the section on Louis XV (see page 79). The wood is machine-carved oak. A few are of walnut—same value. See Price Guide entry no. 75.

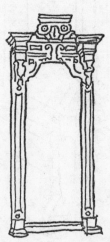

76. Of oak with walnut veneer, this hall mirror is five feet high and contains a sheet of beveled plate glass. See Price Guide entry no. 76.

77. A classic Eastlake bed that is a drug on the market and probably always will be, for the same reason that the Renaissance beds are: too big, and very few antique appreciators go so far as to sleep in them. See Price Guide entry no. 77.

78. Merely a variation of the preceding bed. See Price Guide entry no. 78.

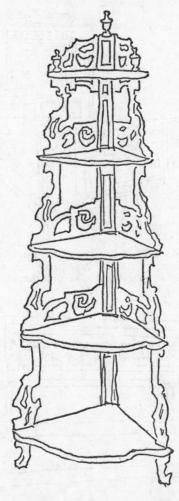

79. The ubiquitous whatnot, picked up from Renaissance and here done in oak, with the tendency toward straighter lines and square corners that typifies the Eastlake style. In the scrollwork there was less of that squareness because it is hard to turn sharp corners with a jigsaw. Probably the whatnot is the piece of Eastlake that has most often found its way into antique shops because it is so useful for displaying small objects. See Price Guide entry no. 79.

80. Hanging shelves of the sort that flooded the country after the Centennial Exposition (see text, page 112) and made all the jigsaw manufacturers in the country rich. These not only were factory-made but also were widely made from patterns by home craftsmen, who ordinarily used walnut because it is easier to work with than oak. See Price Guide entry no. 80.

81. One Eastlake version of the marble-top table. There were many different styles—four-legged, three-legged, tripod. The country has had marble-top fever for the last 15 years, and it shows no signs of abating. See Price Guide entry no. 81.

82. A settee to end all settees, this is the one that put settees out of business. It is a complete negation of Eastlake's original idea that furniture should be strong and useful, designed for the function to which it would be put. This change of idea dates it as being late in the Eastlake period and bodes ill for its increase in value. See Price Guide entry no. 82.

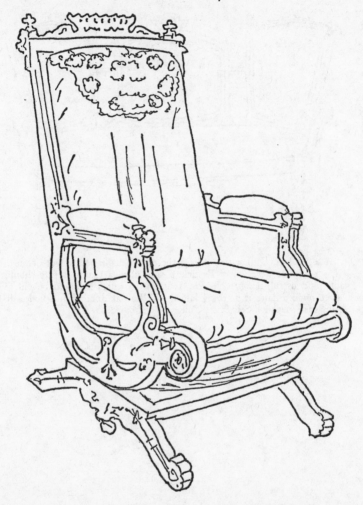

83. These were the days when the platform rocker really came into its own. The base and the chair are separate units connected only with springs, so that the chair rocks back and forth on the base. The original purpose of this arrangement was to prevent rockers from wearing out your rugs, but they also had the appeal of what we would nowadays call a "gimmick." Pieces like this were very strongly made (of oak), and they rock as well today as when first made. See Price Guide entry no. 83.

84. Eastlake also found its way into the plusher offices of the period. This chair rises on a steel screw and tilts back on a spring movement. Piano chairs and stools were also made, but they did not tilt back. See Price Guide entry no. 84.

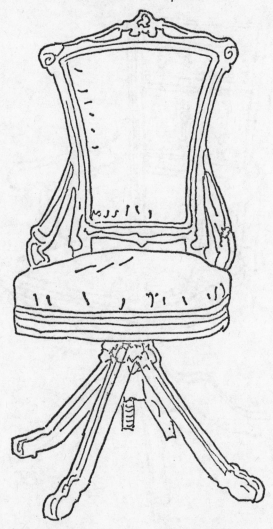

85. Here is a chair, adjustable in height and well upholstered, that was used as a desk or piano chair. It does not tilt back as the preceding chair does. See Price Guide entry no. 85.

86. This is as close to a classic Eastlake chair as you can get. There were many styles of Eastlake chairs, but the basic, characteristic lines to look for are pictured here. The chair is based on squares and rectangles, as opposed to circles and ovals. To borrow a term from music, it is "nervous," has no glides or swirls or roundness. Beautifully fitted of oak parts, this chair still is stronger than any comparable chair you can buy today. See Price Guide entry no. 86.

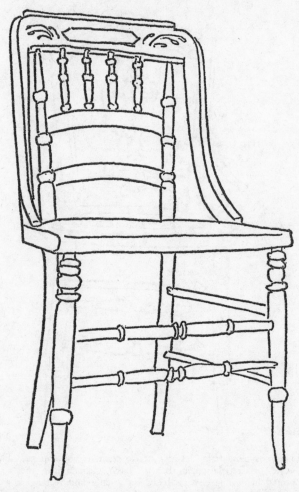

87. One of the hundreds of variations on the basic chair shown previously. It goes a long way from Eastlake but still retains the flavor. See Price Guide entry no. 87.

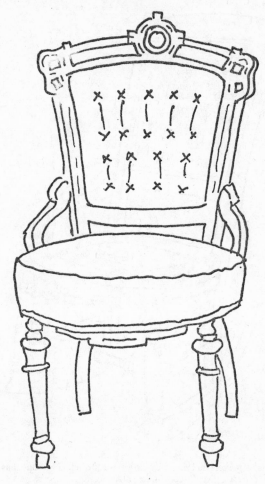

88. A parlor chair with black horsehair upholstery. As with the second chair preceding, it is a classic of the style. See Price Guide entry no. 88.

89. An Eastlake rocker that is still sturdy and strong. This one has been in daily use for decades. See Price Guide entry no. 89.

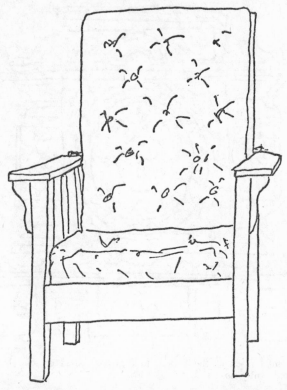

90. I suppose it is pretty cowardly to sneak this chair in here, near the end of the section, in the hope that nobody will notice that it looks more like Mission than like Eastlake. The trouble is that it is a Morris chair, definitely part of the Eastlake excitement. Also it preceded Mission by a decade. The feature of this chair was that the back could be tilted backwards or forwards to suit your mood by means of moving a brass bar in notches cut in extensions of the arms behind the back. The wood was oak, the upholstery usually black-leather cushions. See Price Guide entry no. 90.

91. A mantel clock of the period. In lacquered wood or solid brass. See Price Guide entry no. 91.

92. The so-called Gone With the Wind Lamp, whose name is based on an anachronism in the film of the same name. The lamp is later, first made just after the Civil War—when a craze for lamps of all kinds swept the country. See Price Guide entry no. 92.

93. Hanging lamp of milk glass and brass. See Price Guide entry no. 93.

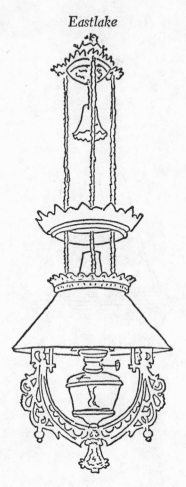

94. White glass and cast iron, brass shade trim. See Price Guide entry no. 94.

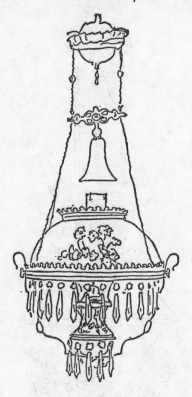

95. Glass and brass, very fancy. See Price Guide entry no. 95.

96. Brass, marble square on base. See Price Guide entry no. 96.

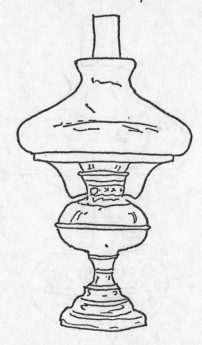

97. Rochester lamp. Brass, green shade. See Price Guide entry no. 97.

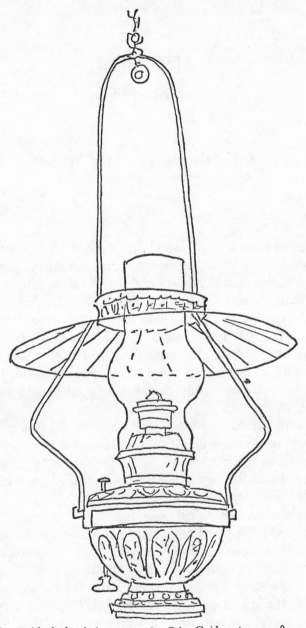

98. Brass with shade of glass pieces. See Price Guide entry no. 98.

16. JACOBEAN
1870–1880

A part of the romantic revival (see Renaissance) that never got very far.

In various comments by Established Authorities on Victorian furniture (none of whose names are mentioned between the covers of this book), you will find that Eastlake got his ideas for furniture from Gothic, Elizabethan, and Jacobean times. Now, I can see where the confusion about Gothic comes in, because the factories that made Eastlake had only a few years before been making Downing's version of Gothic, and ideas have a way of hanging around. Having some old Gothic moldings handy, some factory managers slapped them on Eastlake's "boxes."

Where the Elizabethan idea comes from I haven't the slightest idea, except that it probably sounded pretty learned. If you think of Victorian furniture as a great pile of scrambled eggs, you probably figure that there won't be anybody around to contradict you.

But the Jacobean idea stems from the fact that, during the basically Eastlake Era, one or more factories did turn out quite a few Jacobean chairs that were pretty exact copies of chairs made in England in the seventeenth century. If anyone knows where, why, or how this came about, information concerning the subject would be appreciated. The educated guess concerning these oak chairs, mostly with cane seats, is that

since the English had been reproducing them for years preceding this time, one of them must have showed up at the Centennial Exposition, where some American manufacturer got
the idea that Jacobean might be the next fad. Bad guess.

99. Some Jacobean chairs were quite faithful copies—such as this one—of the Jacobean style as it existed in Europe. This example was of solid oak, with only a light-brown stain, the seat and back caned. See Price Guide entry no. 99.

100. Approximately the same chair as shown in the preceding illustration, except that this one was upholstered in leather on the seat and back. See Price Guide entry no. 100.

101. This chair is derivative of the Jacobean style, but it does get a little
florid and Frenchy. Also, the wood was mahogany, and the seat was inlaid
with mother-of-pearl. See Price Guide entry no. 101.

17. ORIENTAL
1875–1900

*Not really a style but a decorative fad
that left few remains.*

Another substyle or side interest of the Eastlake-to-fretwork
years was furniture of an Oriental and, especially, Turkish
cast. Interest in the Orient can be seen to have already started
with Chippendale, who made some very Chinese-looking furniture, and with Sheraton, who got his idea for the ottoman from the piles of rugs the Turks used to sit on instead of chairs. These ideas obviously were brought back by
the trading and whaling vessels that were roaming the world
in those days.

Interest in things oriental reached its height in the late
1880s and was coincident with the heyday of Tiffany ware
and mother-of-pearl inlays on anything that was handy. Some
people credit Whistler and the current French school of painters with starting the fad, but, at any rate, the ladies' magazines of the time picked it up and promoted the idea of the
Turkish or Japanese "corner," without which any drawing
room was *déclassée*.

Very little Oriental has survived, and because many of the
pieces used were authentic it is more reasonable to classify
them as the product of some Tang dynasty than as Victorian. About the only furniture made in America for this craze
were some bamboo chairs, and I enter it in this narrative only
for completeness and more to deny it as a furniture style than
anything else.

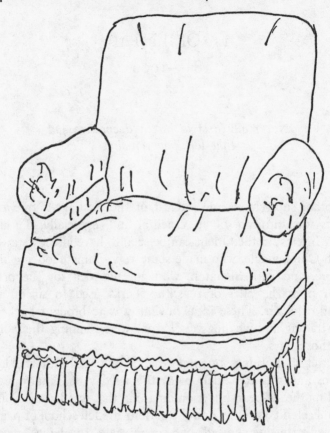

102. Because it is all upholstery, it is patently impossible to restore a piece like this Turkish sort of chair. By now the material is so decomposed that it all has to be replaced, and what you really are doing when you reupholster it is reproducing it. The demand for pieces like this is so small that it is impossible to give them a market value, and they are included only in the interest of completeness. At auctions it frequently happens that no one will even bid on them. See Price Guide entry no. 102.

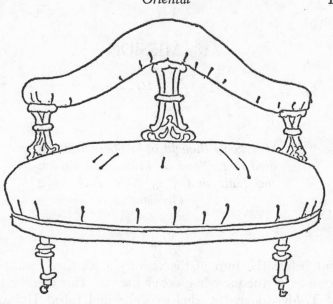

103. This piece of overstuffed whatever-you-want-to-call-it is more reasonable than the preceding piece, because there is some woodwork showing and the shape of the "pillows" does have considerable character. It is a decorator's item and can be used only in a really sophisticated room as a conversation piece—or, as the boys would say, "for fun." See Price entry no. 103.

18. MISSION

1895–1910

Mistakenly thought of as Spanish, it was sired in England by Morris and Ruskin and built mostly in New York by a German.

Just before the turn of the century a reaction against the fussiness of the preceding decades set in. This was the time of Teddy Roosevelt's wholesomeness and Elbert Hubbard's promotion of the simple things in life. Architecturally, the country was swept by the bungalow style. This called for simple, inexpensive houses featuring exposed beams in the ceilings of the living rooms, overhanging roofs, and front porches usually supported by columns of boulders set in cement.

Of course, a lot of people were involved in this turn of events, but the most important was a writer, editor, designer, and manufacturer named Gustav Stickley. He designed and promoted bungalow houses (the predecessor of the ranch house of today) and singlehanded designed and manufactured a style of furniture to go into them. This was the simple, strong, functional, ugly Mission style.

He sent this stuff out by the carload from Binghamton, New York, and it was soon imitated by other manufacturers and widely sold by Sears, Roebuck and Company.

Mission Furniture was made of solid-oak boards stained dark brown and put together with such integrity of design and workmanship that about the only way you can break it is to run over it with a tank. It was a perfect expression of the idea prevalent at the time, that what America needed was a return to simplicity, the outdoor life, wholesome books, and all that sort of thing, an idea typified by "Teddy," who was already a popular national figure and would soon become President.

Stickley's original term for his furniture was "Craftsman," but this name was lost in the shuffle when, as the bungalow style spread across the country, a Chicago builder-promoter named Wilson rechristened the house Spanish Mission. The name obviously came to him out of the blue, but the term had a romantic appeal, and it stuck—to the furniture, too.

As to the future of Mission, it is hard to imagine as this is being written that anyone in his right mind will ever collect it. It may be sincere, wholesome, and functional as all get-out, but its lines are ponderous and oppressive. It rudely intrudes itself and dominates a room like a policeman in uniform. As time goes by, however, so do our evaluations in these matters. Style after style has been rejected, only to be picked up and cherished after years have gone by. So, who knows? Perhaps some day Mission will be scraped down to the natural oak, bleached, reupholstered in something lighter than the original black leather, and sold as "Early American Modern"—which of course it was, being an obvious predecessor of today's modern, squared-up, foam-rubber-topped designs.

104. I realize that the idea of anyone buying a piece of Mission Furniture is pretty far-fetched. Certainly you will never find it (yet!) in an antique shop. But it certainly was a well-defined style of furniture and has to be included in any survey of furniture styles popular during the life-span of Queen Victoria—not to mention the growth of American taste in design. Also, those of us who can remember when you could pick up a Renaissance marble-top table of solid walnut for two or three dollars are very leery of saying that there is any kind of old furniture that won't become popular in time. If this ever happens to Mission—and my guess is that it will happen in Manhattan in about ten years—these little desks (solid oak, stained dark brown) will probably be the first pieces to become popular. Little desks are always the most sought-after piece in any style. See Price Guide entry no. 104.

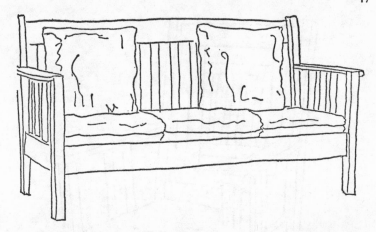

105. Heavy and solid are about the nicest things you can say about Mission Furniture. Even the black-leather cushions and pillows that were always used were so well made that they are still serviceable. As with all Mission, this piece was of solid oak stained a depressing dark brown. When they "come in," these pieces will probably be sold only after the oak has been bleached to its natural color—at which point they would undeniably have a certain modern look. See Price Guide entry no. 105.

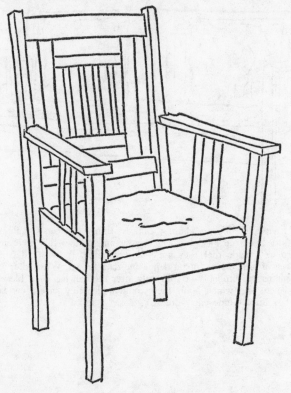

106. A Mission chair! See Price Guide entry no. 106.

19. GOLDEN OAK

1900–1915

*Sister to Mission, it was also an issue of
the Ruskin-Morris emphasis on strength
and simplicity of line.*

The fairly random style that we are classifying here as Golden
Oak sprang from the same roots as Mission. That is to say,
it also was a reaction against the ornateness of the preceding
decades. But Golden Oak was a more generalized style and
cannot be traced as particularly as Mission can to a particular designer. It was "factory-designed" to meet a popular
taste and demand. This was the same demand that Mission
answered, and rather than repeat the generalities made in that
section, we suggest that you turn back a few pages and read
them in the original.

As to construction, however, Golden Oak was considerably
more sophisticated than Mission, and it is slightly easier to
break. You don't need a tank, a truck will do. Also the sections
—as with pedestal tables—were sometimes bolted together instead of being fitted and glued. In fact, sometimes even ve-
neering was done, and that is getting pretty effete. This was
a veneer of even-grained oak on a core of small pieces of
oak of inferior quality.

Of considerably less-dominating lines than Mission, Golden
Oak has already become popular with artistically sophisticated
people.

From the point of view of value, this style is already well

established (see captions on the following pages) and will continue to rise in popularity. How fast and how high it will rise is, of course, impossible to predict.

107. The pedestal table is at the heart of the Golden Oak craze. Recently a dealer from Dallas bought every one he could find in New Bedford and environs and filled a moving van before returning to Texas. If you ask why they are so popular, the answer invariably is that they "go with modern." See Price Guide entry no. 107.

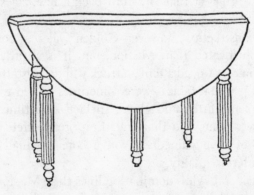

108. The drop-leaf table in oak is as yet nowhere nearly as popular as the pedestal table, but it is certainly "coming in" in the sophisticated, intellectual centers—the big cities and the university towns. See Price Guide entry no. 108.

109. These fancy-legged tables were quite popular. About the size of a card table. Oak with glass ball and claw feet. See Price Guide entry no. 109.

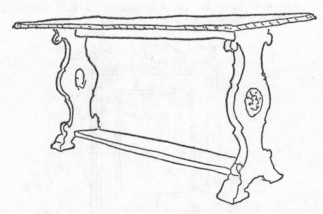

110. The library or study table—just the thing for displaying your magazines. Still largely unappreciated (especially by me), these are good for filling up the space in a summer cottage. See Price Guide entry no. 110.

111. The legs are some kind of horn brought back from a safari, and I call this a Teddy Roosevelt table. Of course, it is a unique piece, but so many wonderfully crazy things like this were done at the time that we have to show at least one example. See Price Guide entry no. 111.

112. Oak towel cabinets are now used as medicine chests. The bar across the bottom was for hanging your towel. The mirrors are of beveled plate glass and usually still perfect. See Price Guide entry no. 112.

113. This chest of drawers was typical of the era. Solid oak, pressed-brass-sheet drawer pulls, grooves running across the fronts of the drawers. Derivative of Eastlake, which sometimes shows in the style of the decorative carving, but not necessarily. See Price Guide entry no. 113.

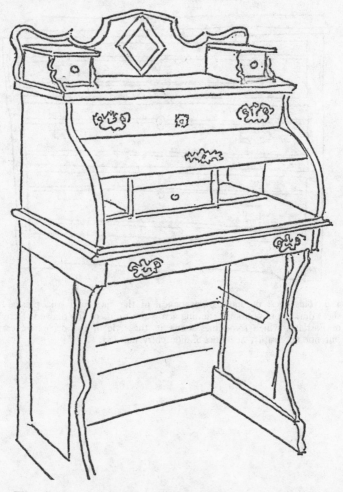

114. The roll top on this desk is a solid piece of wood, and the whole thing is certainly derivative of Eastlake. See Price Guide entry no. 114.

115. The roll top of this desk is made of slats glued to canvas, as opposed
to that of the preceding model. Some of the lines are reminiscent of Eastlake,
but the pressed-brass drawer-pull shields and the characteristic grooving across
the drawer front establish this desk firmly in the era of Golden Oak. See
Price Guide entry no. 115.

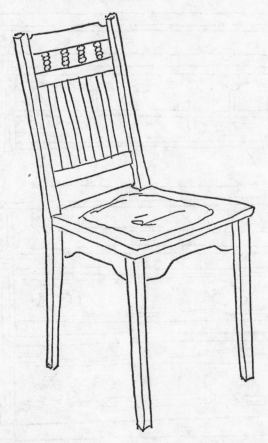

116. From Eastlake, Golden Oak developed in two directions. One was toward simplification, as shown in this chair and in the further development shown in the following small office chair. For the other direction, see the second chair following. See Price Guide entry no. 116.

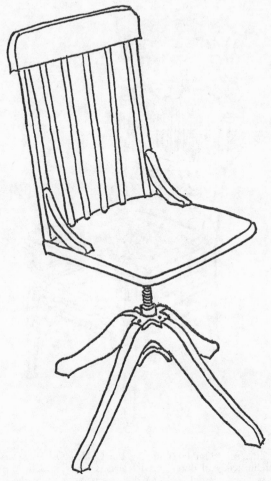

117. Like the pedestal table that begins this section, this office chair is so simple that it "fits in with modern." See Price Guide entry no. 117.

118. The other direction taken during the Golden Oak Era was toward a general, undirected, and disorganized fanciness, as typified by this oak chair with cane seat and pressed back. (A design was pressed into the back with a metal die in simulation of carving. You can recognize this by the fact that the indentations are very shallow and the end grain of the wood has not been exposed in the indentations as it would have been by a carving knife.) See Price Guide entry no. 118.

119. Another example of the trend toward simplicity through functional design in the Golden Oak Era. The desk is oak, with cast-iron legs, adjustable for height. The seat and back of the chair are oak, but the rest cast iron. Both, of course, were used in schools and screwed to the floor. See Price Guide entry no. 119.

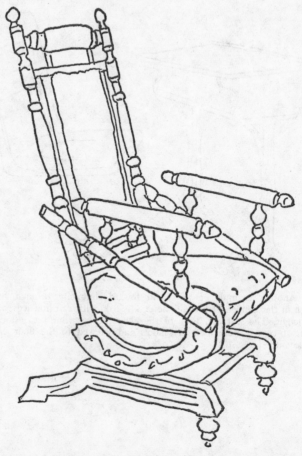

120. In this era the platform rocker went into mass production, as evidenced by this chair made of turnings off an automatic lathe. (Compare the piece with the chair on page 126, in the section on Eastlake.) The heavy sections were still cut out of oak, but the turnings were of maple, birch, poplar, or any other hardwood suitable for lathe work. (Oak can be turned but has a tendency to split and chip, and so was avoided.) See Price Guide entry no. 120.

121. An oak table of no particular character or significance. Nevertheless, a lot like this one were made. See Price Guide entry no. 121.

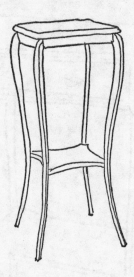

122. A plant stand of the same genre as the table preceding. See Price Guide entry no. 122.

123. An oak mantel clock, mass-produced. Notice that the case proper is reminiscent of a much earlier period. Around this has been glued a sheet of ornately carved oak. The case and base are also of oak. See Price Guide entry no. 123.

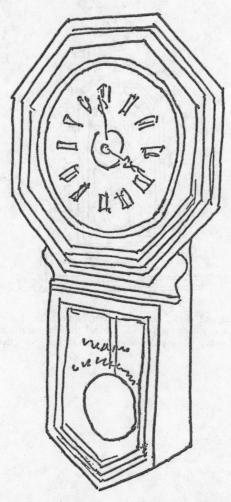

124. The hanging wall clock was another particularly popular piece during
this era. Once cleaned, it still works well, once you get it hanging at just
the right angle on your wall. (Clocks like this often have to be slanted a
few degrees one way or the other.) See Price Guide entry no. 124.

125. This decoration was cast in plaster of Paris, then beautifully painted and glazed. It is typical of the romanticism in the art of the era. See Price Guide entry no. 125.

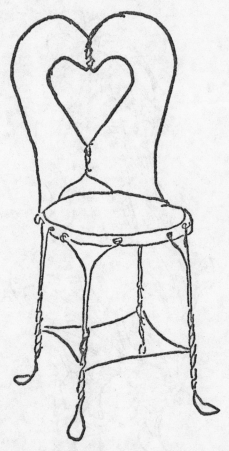

126. The ice-cream chair is one antique that has gone down in price because of having been widely reproduced in recent years. It takes an expert eye to tell them apart, and to do so you have to look under the seat to see the slight difference. See Price Guide entry no. 126.

127. Brass beds are still going to the town dump, but I'd like to have a barnful of them. So far they are only selling to the arty crowd in the big cities, but they are destined to go a lot higher. See Price Guide entry no. 127.

128. Phonographs are a specialty of some collectors. The horn is brass, and polished up it is a sight to see indeed! See Price Guide entry no. 128.

129. Standard colored-glass hanging lamp. In this shade, the glass pieces fit into a brass frame. See Price Guide entry no. 129.

20. ART NOUVEAU

1895–1910

*The idea that furniture should look as if
it were growing. Only the very rich could
afford it.*

In contrast to the sensibility and wholesomeness of the Mission and Golden Oak styles, the turn of the century also saw a minor craze for a style of furniture that strains the credulity of a healthy mind. This was Art Nouveau; the idea was that the lines and structural patterns occurring in nature must be the purest, the strongest, and most beautiful. To return to them was supposed to be a return to the fundamentals of life. Art Nouveau followed these lines and patterns, with the result that chairs and other pieces looked as if they were growing out of the floor.

That the whole idea was ridiculous doesn't seem to have occurred to anybody at the time. This development is relatively unimportant in the history of American furniture design, however. It was fundamentally a European craze that was picked up only by the very wealthy, who were in the habit of sailing back and forth across the Atlantic Ocean.

The only real impact that Art Nouveau made in this country was in the field of what we would call gift items—vases, little boxes, lamps, frames, and some jewelry. Some of these were mass-produced and atrocious, but many were very finely designed and made by Tiffany and his imitators and rivals.

In the field of furniture, pieces are so rare that there is

no established market for them, and the style is included in this book only in the interest of completeness.

Now, why a style with a French name and general-European origin (not exclusively French) is included in our section on English Influence—well, that's a good question! The best answer I can think of is that the style was only a novelty that was picked up and used by a society that was by that time under the influence of English rather than French ideas and culture.

Art Nouveau Furniture was made entirely of metal. It usually was made of cast sections bolted together, but sometimes sheet stampings were made and attached to the frame. The metal was most often brass (expensive stuff!) but sometimes was iron. In some cases the pieces were enameled in their natural colors—green leaves, brown vines, yellow and purple flowers. Wow!

130. This fantasy is made entirely of metal—tubing for the main stalks and castings for the flowers and fruit. Some people may think this kind of furniture was a joke, but it was far from it. It was very expensive even in its time, and a bed such as this was far more beautifully executed than my drawing shows. Of this style, very little was made, and probably all of it in France. Why, then, call it (American) Victorian? Well, mainly because it was made for rich Americans—very rich Americans—of the kind who in those days were always traveling back and forth from Paris. It definitely was the rage in America among the sophisticated and wealthy.

Today the market for a bed like this may be extremely small, but the supply is even smaller. See Price Guide entry no. 130.

131. Well, *chacun à son goût*, as the French always say. See the previous caption for notes on construction and materials used. Again the price depends upon the person who wants it, and where the piece is found. See Price Guide entry no. 131.

132. If this lamp somehow reminds you of Tiffany, it should, because Art Nouveau was of the same period of taste. Brass stems and colored-glass leaves, and glass fruit on the brass make this lamp a sight to behold, especially when the whole is lit up with colored bulbs. See Price Guide entry no. 132.

21. REFINISHING VICTORIAN

Concerning that "ol' debbil" lye—and
some much easier methods of removing
Victorian finishes.

A lot of people who are just starting out in this mildly insane business of collecting antiques have a tendency to shy
away from buying pieces "in the rough." It always looks like
too much work if they are going to refinish the piece themselves, or too expensive to have someone else do it. But this
is a case where ignorance isn't bliss—it's expensive. They are
missing all the best buys. And this is because "in the rough"
covers a lot of territory and a wide range of surface condi-
tions. Sure, I'll admit that some pieces are in such bad shape
that to clean them up you'd have to make a career of it. But
there are also many pieces that can be restored in a half hour
or less if you are able to recognize them and you know the
tricks of the trade that the professionals use.

To get the worst aspect of this business out of the way
first, let's start with the pieces that have been painted. There
is no getting around the fact that eight layers of well-seasoned
paint do present a problem. Removing them is a major job
that involves a couple of gallons of paint remover—or, if you
are courageous, a summer afternoon in your back yard with
a bucket of lye.

In case you are interested, my own secret formula for using
lye is this:

1 scant quart of water
1 can of lye crystals
wallpaper paste to thicken
1 quart of cheapest vinegar or Clorox
1 handy garden hose

Use an enamel or stainless-steel pot or a galvanized pail. Never aluminum. If you use an aluminum container, you will be setting up a miniature chemical plant that will manufacture a poison gas in copious quantities. (The same thing happens when you try to make soap in an aluminum pot. And if you thought that the last of the poeple who make their own soap died out years ago, well, then, baby, you just haven't been to Vermont lately! Or the Lower East Side of New York City, either.)

To avoid a volcanic eruption, put the water in the pail first and pour the lye in while you stir the water with a stick at least eighteen inches long; even when you sprinkle the lye crystals into the water, you will get considerable activity down there in the pail.

In a minute or so, the boiling will stop, and you can sprinkle your wallpaper paste (ordinary wheat paste) into the lye water a handful at a time until it reaches the consistency of a creamy paint remover.

To apply this inexpensive and, believe me, highly potent slop to your painted piece of furniture, use a two-foot stick to the end of which you have wired a handful of six-inch-long strips of rag. (It will eat the bristles off a brush in forty-five seconds flat!)

For best results, work in the sun on a warm day, out of the wind. The effectiveness of lye is in direct ratio to its degree of heat. On a cold winter day, for instance, nothing happens.

To give you a rough idea, this mixture should soften four layers of paint in about ten to fifteen minutes. Now rinse the piece with your handy hose, and scrape the bulk of the paint off. Scrub the rest off with an ordinary bristle scrubbing brush.

Finally, wipe any remaining moisture off the piece with rags, and let dry for half an hour or so. Then, using a paint-brush, soak the whole piece with undiluted vinegar. This is to neutralize any of the lye left in the cracks and crevices of the piece; traces of lye would gum up the shellac or varnish that you might want to apply to the piece in the future.

Incidentally, lye will turn any wood a rich dark brown—which many people find highly desirable. But if you aren't one of that congenial crowd, you can use any liquid laundry bleach (of the Clorox genus) instead of the vinegar. This will neutralize the lye just as well as the vinegar will and also bleach the wood back to its lightest natural shade.

After a ten-minute soaking, the vinegar or Clorox should also be washed off with your handy hose, and when thoroughly dry, your piece is ready for refinishing.

But now we come to the part that's fun. Ninety per cent of Victorian furniture hasn't been refinished, and many a piece that looks as if it has spent the last fifty years in a chicken coop can be restored to glory as quickly as Jack Horner pulled out his plum.

Sometimes plain soap and water is the first step, but not very often, and don't expect too much of it. Although soap and water will remove oil and dirt, it won't touch wax—into which most dirt has usually worked. So the big cleaner is plain old-fashioned turpentine, because it *does* dissolve and remove the dirty, dull wax.

All right, you say, but what if the piece still looks dull, lifeless, scuffed, scratched, worn, hazy-white, alligatored, and a few other things?

Well, there is a magic answer, because all these ills can be cured by one simple, fast, easy trick. All you have to do is to trot down to your paint and hardware store and pick up

1 pint of lacquer thinner
1 pint of denatured alcohol
(sometimes labeled "shellac solvent").

When you get home from the store, take out two coffee cups and set up your finish-restoring laboratory by pouring a little alcohol in one cup and a little lacquer thinner in the other. Take a one-inch-square pad of cotton cloth and wet it first in the alcohol. Now lightly rub a small section of the spoiled finish. If the finish is pure shellac—as about half the finishes are—the immediate results will amaze your friends and confound your enemies. The finish will become crystal clear and the color and figure of the wood will show through.

What you now do is to make a larger pad—about three inches square and six or seven layers thick—with which you wipe down the whole piece. Just wipe until the finish comes back. If you wipe too long or too hard in one spot you will eventually wipe the finish off completely.

The next step is to let the piece dry for an hour. Then you rub it down lightly with ooo-grade steel wool to cut down the glare and eliminate streaks left by your wiping pad. Apply wax or furniture polish, and invite your aforementioned friends and enemies over to your house to observe what a remarkably clever person you really are.

As to the lacquer thinner, I suppose you could use it to remove your old nail polish, but more to the point would be to pour it back in the can and save it until you get a piece of furniture that the alcohol doesn't work on. Try the lacquer thinner in that event—proceeding in all details the same way as you do with alcohol.

The third possibility is that neither the wood alcohol nor the lacquer thinner works—which happens in only about 5 or 10 per cent of the cases. You then mix the two ingredients together in one cup—a 50-50 mixture. This will work, all right, because it will take any antique finish off the way

Grant took Richmond, but quite easily and neatly. This is nothing like the messy job you undertake when you go at something with paint remover. You just wet the surface thoroughly and wipe off the finish first with dry rags, and then finish up with a rag that has been dipped in your mixture and squeezed out. (Aside from drying your hands out pretty thoroughly, neither denatured alchohol nor lacquer thinner will hurt them.)

After you have cleaned the old finish off this way, no new finish need be applied. All you have to do is let the piece dry for an hour and wax for a beautiful sheen, which will bring out all the color and figure of the wood.

For further instructions on restoring, refinishing, and repairing antiques, I can heartily recommend another book, *The Furniture Doctor*. By coincidence the author's name is also George Grotz—exactly the same as mine.

PART III

APPENDIX

22. HOW THE ANTIQUE BUSINESS WORKS

A guided tour behind the scenes with the author and his infamous Uncle George. An irreverent but practical guide for anyone who has ever thought about going into the antique business.

Shakespeare or somebody once said that some men are born great, others achieve greatness, and there are always a few poor dopes in every generation that have it thrust upon them. Well, let's get it straight right from the beginning that that's the way this dope got into the antique business. I wasn't born to it. I certainly didn't try to get into it. Of course, now that we're here, I don't deny that I've gotten a few laughs out of it and even a living of sorts. But I want it clearly understood that I am not the kind that gets mushy-eyed over a broken-down old cobbler's bench or even a ratty Victorian ottoman. (Five will get you ten that the cobbler's bench is a fake, anyway!)

I got into the antique business through the back door. Namely, by refinishing antiques for some rich antique dealers around Essex, Connecticut, who were all firmly convinced that the only good refinisher is a hungry refinisher.

Well, when I got inside the back door I found out that the secret of the antique business was to buy things cheap enough and sell them dear enough, so that you can pay your rent and still have something left over. The more left over the better. Was I amazed! Here I had been thinking that those quaint little antique shops along the highway were a romantic way of life, and just lots of fun for elderly folk enjoying their golden years.

Boy, did I have a wrong number! Antiques are not groceries or something that people line up to buy on a Friday evening outside your shop. You've got to *sell* them. Furthermore, the people who buy antiques are not simple but the most indefatigable shoppers in the world. Also, the fellow down the road has sent his old aunt up as a spy to find out your prices and is asking 5 per cent less for the same things you have. On top of that, there are things like capital investment, rate of turnover, percentage of your draw from the surplus as opposed to what has to go back into new stock, finding new stock, doing your own patching, repairing, and refinishing— and so on. It's a complicated business.

But it can be a profitable business—and even an enjoyable one—for the right kind of people. Which gives us a good place to start getting down to brass tacks: What kind of people can and do succeed in the antique business?

From what I have seen, the people most likely to succeed in the antique business are those who don't like antiques. Of course, this is only a partial truth. But the dealer I know who makes the most money goes home every night from his enormous shop to a living room full of picture windows, plain modern furniture, and some kind of chair his wife bought him that has buttons on it to change him to different positions, to vibrate him or heat him up, and whatever else it does.

Now if I sound like a cynic or a mocker, I don't mean it that way. As I see it, a man or woman who has been successful in any other business can be successful in the antique business. A love of antiques is not necessary. It may not hurt, but it isn't necessary. All that is necessary is that you understand them and have a mind like an adding machine to judge how much you should pay and how much you have to get to make a profit.

In other words, you don't have to love antiques, but you do have to love doing business. Or trading, or keeping shop or whatever you want to call it. If you don't feel that way, try something else. Maybe making antiques—which is also a good trade.

Another aspect of the *kind* of person who succeeds is that a liking for keeping books will be helpful. You simply have to have a way of knowing at the end of the year whether you made or lost money *after* deduction of the cost of your product plus operating expenses. Incidentally, tax collectors don't think antique shops are quaint, romantic little places either. To them you're just another stop, and they *never* drive by.

How much capital do you need to go into the antique business? That, of course, depends on how much business you intend to do or how much of your income you want to make out of the business. With many people it is just a side line to supplement other income. Also, many people go into it gradually—which is probably the best way to go into any business, because if in the first or second year you flop at it, you lose less time (and money) that way.

But for a point of reference, let's suppose you and your wife are retired and want to make an additional $2000 a year out of what is, after all, a pretty pleasant occupation.

One way to look at it is that to make $2000 a year you are going to have to have a stock worth $2000 and turn it over twice a year—charging, on the average, twice as much for each item as you paid for it. (This is where you have to keep records, because on some things you can only make 10 per cent, whereas in the case of a table you have repaired and refinished you may be able to get back sixty-five dollars on an original ten-dollar investment.)

First you buy $1000 worth of antiques at wholesale. You

sell them for $2000 in six months, and you've made $1000. Do it again in the same year, and you've made another $1000. Of course this buying and selling is a continuous process, and I am assuming you are not paying any rent. But that is the general idea. Not romantic. Just like Macy's or Gimbels.

Now another factor in this is, that how much stock you can sell a year also depends on how many people are coming in and out of your shop in a year. In other words, on your location. This has to be found out by trying it. But, roughly speaking, the best location for an antique shop is not next to another antique shop—it is right between two others. Or, even better, on a whole block of them. Or in a town where there are a lot of other shops. Antique shops don't sell to people in their local area but to antique hunters and tourists who roam far and wide. And they will seek out any congregation of shops far more often than they will the shop that has a monopoly in a town or area.

Now, I can hear the objections all over the place to this. I will bet that every reader of these words knows of a shop in which the stock is obviously worth $10,000 and the little old lady running it—or the golden-age couple—is obviously only making a bare living out of the place.

I have two answers to this:

1. When the little old lady dies, everyone will be amazed to find out that she had a million dollars in the bank from way back.

2. The little old lady loved antiques and hated to part with them, so she kept her prices so high that nobody would buy them.

Another thing that makes for success in the antique business is being handy. For one thing, about half the good buys you get will be low priced because someone else is too lazy or not handy enough to fix them up. Another thing is that the broken-down, the busted, and the cracked will give you something to do in your off-season months. Something, that is, besides flying down to Rio to spend your ill-gained profits in high living. Fixing up antiques, of course, is a matter of bred-in-the-bone talent, and if you are not handy now, if you are not already known as a fixer-upper, don't think that all you have to do is make up your mind to learn. Some learn, some don't.

The basic equipment you need, then, to go into the antique business is the following:

1. Money.
2. (Preferably) a dislike for antiques.
3. A station wagon. For obvious reasons.
4. The tools and other stuff for a general fix-it shop.
5. A quaint little house by the side of the road, preferably with a bay window, ivy, etc.

The next question—and it's a big one—is where do antique dealers get all that junk? I mean stuff. All right—lovely things.

BUYING CONTENTS

The best way to acquire antiques is to buy "contents"—the entire contents of a house. How you find these, we'll come to in a minute, but the reason this is the best way is that for some strange reason people will take a lot less for things in an aggregate than they will for things sold individually. Try it on your own house sometime. First, just guess what the entire contents are worth. Then go around putting a price on each piece, and add all the prices up. I guarantee that you'll be amazed at the difference.

What you then do with the conglomeration of junk you have bought is to pick out what you can use and sell the rest to a junk man—which will get you back a good part of

your capital investment right away. (But, see, always the
bookkeeping has to go on!)

And here's a special tip that I got from an Ohio dealer
whom I met at an antique show in Poughkeepsie or some-
place: Act a little dumb (well, do that all the time) and always ask the seller if there are any specially good pieces in the
lot. You know, pieces whose value you might not recognize
because you are just a beginner in the business or a simple
country boy or whatever. Invariably there will be something
that the seller thinks is just the world's best but which is
really a hunk of junk. It may be a three-dollar rocker that
Aunt Minnie thought Abraham Lincoln slept in. Or a "valuable" old grandfather's clock that Uncle Tobias got at an
auction once but that is really a cheap Grand Rapids reproduction.

You accept their valuation, however. But when you give
your price—say, $500 for the lot—holding a great wad of green-
backs in your hand as you speak—then say, "For everything
except the clock, of course." In that way, you avoid paying
cash for their sentiment, and you make them think you are
honest by going on with some malarky about the clock being so good that you can't fairly estimate its worth. You say
you want them to get the top price from some other dealer
qualified to appreciate it. This will really clinch the buy for
you, because the seller can immediately see from this fair
attitude of yours that you have his interest at heart and
couldn't possibly offer less for the rest of the stuff than it
is worth.

FINDING CONTENTS

Now as to how you find houses full of stuff to buy, the
obvious first step is to run a year-round classified ad in all the
weekly papers within a fifty-mile radius. The ad includes the
line "We buy contents."

But that's not nearly enough. The next step is to make friends with all the real estate dealers, bankers, and lawyers that you can, because they will know when houses are being sold and their contents will need disposing of. You will also do well to suggest to these citizens that, if they help you get leads, you will be able to help them or in some way return the favor.

On top of this, you must become an avid reader of real estate news and (let's face it) obituary columns. And don't overlook the business properties in the real estate news. If you can get the contents of an old hotel for, say, twenty dollars a room, you can really turn a profit.

WHERE THE ANTIQUES ARE

The second basic way to get stock is to import it. The fundamental fact behind this is that antiques come onto the market in economically depressed areas—which means that the population of the area is declining or at least not increasing. Even if people aren't moving out of the area and the population is not declining but is static, young people who are getting married will be trying to move into new houses. Even if they live in old houses, they will want to "get rid of that old junk." Junk that you and I just happen to be crazy enough to look at as valuable merchandise.

Now, these areas are of two kinds: first, rural areas where the small farmer is finding it impossible to make a living. The obvious ones are Maine, New Hampshire, Vermont, and northern New York. With the exception of California and Florida, such areas can be found in every state of the Union.

In the second kind of area, industries have become obsolete or factories have moved out of town for one reason or another. Cities and towns where these things are happening exist in almost every state. Right now the outstanding exam-

ple is central Massachusetts, which is losing its textile industry and others to the South, where labor costs are cheaper.

If you think this is highfalutin theorizing, believe me, it
isn't. I knew one woman with a shop in Connecticut (the
ritzy part) who bought about half of her stuff on a spring
trip through Vermont, and ordered the rest—*sight unseen*—by
mail from a wholesaler outside Providence, Rhode Island—another state that is good pickings.

How do you go about buying in such areas? That's easy.
In every such place there will already be established antique
dealers and junk dealers who will sell at either retail or wholesale. You don't need any certification that you are a dealer.
All you need is the willingness to part with four or five hundred dollars in cash. These men are realists. They are such
realists that you can even trust them not to cheat you. In
fact, they will educate you about values for free. This is because you are their bread and butter and they want you to
make money on their stuff so that you will come back next
year.

Such wholesalers are easy to find in and around big cities
because they advertise. They don't advertise that they sell
for wholesale. That you have to find out by going and talking to them.

As to buying in rural areas (from which, naturally, come
a class of antiques of a more rural nature), this is more dif-
ficult, because the sources are harder to find. They are all
over the place, but they don't hang out signs. They don't need
to, because they usually have clients coming to them every
spring to take everything they have gathered. This is why a
dealer will limit himself to one small rural area and go to
the same place year after year to get his "country" antiques.
It takes time to get to know the ropes and make contacts.
But concentrated attention will soon become far more pro-
ductive than roaming all over the place.

IMPORT-EXPORT—U.S.A.

A final aspect of "importing" as a source of merchandise is that it is often possible to buy at retail from an antique shop in one part of the country and sell the same items for twice as much in another part of the country. For one thing, the retail prices of all antiques are higher in and around cities than they are out in the boondocks—at least at the times of year when the tourists aren't around. Then there is also the matter of popularity or taste. The rising interest in Victorian furniture, for instance, is still pretty spotty. The trick is to transport it from a place where it is still considered junk to one where it is appreciated. For instance, Empire is valued far more highly down South than it is in New England. Eastlake is sneered at in Boston but highly "appreciated" in Nebraska. These differences in evaluation go for hundreds of times and are the reason behind the old joke that most antique dealers seem to make their livings off each other.

Variations in taste almost always have something to do with the history of a particular part of the country. One of the best examples is an ox yoke being worth about four times as much in Texas as it is in Connecticut. It seems that, back when oxen were doing all the heavy hauling, Connecticut was the place where most of them were raised for sale throughout New England and neighboring New York State. As a result, the barns of Connecticut were—and in some spots still are—rotten with yokes. And it follows that if a thing is plentiful it is not highly valued.

On the other hand, in Texas—and other parts of the Southwest—there are practically no ox yokes lying around. This is because, as soon as the settlers got their covered wagons out (hauled by oxen, of course), they switched to horses to do their hauling. Horses were faster, and since the roads were drier the oxen's superiority in mud wasn't so important any more. But nowadays, you see, Texans have a very special interest in yokes because they are a symbol of the first families to arrive by wagon train. Everybody in Texas who had a great-granddaddy who arrived by wagon train wants an ox yoke on the wall, so that whoever comes into their house won't think that they are Johnny-come-latelies to the Golden West.

So, as they always say about stamp collecting, the antique business can be downright educational!

HOW TO BUY AT AUCTIONS

Going down the line of sources, we next come to the one that holds the least chance of making a killing but is certainly the most fun—namely, auctions.

To begin with, let's dispel the ridiculous notion that dealers drive prices up when they bid at auctions. Nothing could be further from the truth. It's the summer people who get the prices way up there, the same summer people who complain about the dealers. I have been in my nefarious career both a summer people and a dealer, so believe me, I know.

It can be proven by simple logic that the dealers don't run the prices up. In the first place, a dealer doesn't go to an auction just for kicks. He is a businessman, and when he starts bidding on a piece, he knows to the exact penny how high he is going to go. And when he gets to his top bid he stops. He can't pay more for a piece than he's going to sell it for at retail. Not to mention that he has to cover his expenses, and make a profit. He doesn't get excited and think he might as well go one more bid. He knows from experience that this way lies disaster. He has had auction fever in the past, but he has conquered it or he wouldn't still be in business.

Furthermore, you will never see two dealers bidding against each other. Two of them may both bid on the same item, but they never get excited, and most of the time one of them will drop out early if he knows that the other fellow can use the piece better than he can. Not because he's altruistic but because he knows the other fellow will return the favor someday. Dealers, like the rest of us, have found out that life is a lot easier if they get along with the other fellows in the same business. They often have little conferences before the auction opens to agree on who does the bidding on what. They talk over how high they are willing to go for a given piece, and the fellow who is willing to go the highest does the bidding. This keeps the bidding more desultory and helps to keep the tourists from getting excited.

Not that dealers haven't on occasion double-crossed each other, but that gets into the realm of anecdotes, and you know how I hate to tell an anecdote.

An auction is the epitome of the free market. It's just like Wall Street—where the fair price of something is determined solely by how much people are willing to pay for it. And just as Wall Street has its good days and its bad days, there are also auctions where things go high and auctions where things go low. Which brings us to the brilliant deduction that the best auction is the one at which you are the only bidder. Naturally this isn't going to happen very often—unless you bribe the auctioneer to advertise his show for the day after it is really going to take place. (And don't think it hasn't happened.) In that event you are going to have to split your ill-gotten gains with the auctioneer. Someone is going to cry murder, and the auctioneer is going to lose his license. And you are both going to have to move to another state. This may or may not be worth your while. It is the sort of major decision you will just have to make for yourself. As the old Chinese proverb goes, "In this life you can have either love or reason. You must choose for yourself."

Getting back to auctions, the point is to find ones that everybody else isn't going to. Auctions in spring and fall, therefore, are better than auctions in the summer. And the spring ones are best, because country people—all people who pay fuel bills, for that matter—are poorer in the spring than in the fall. That is why it is best to make a buying trip in the spring.

That doesn't mean that there aren't any good (low-priced) auctions in the summer. Here the trick is to pray for rain or a cold snap on the day the auction is advertised for. It's a case of the bargains falling to him who braves the storm.

If you have a lot of nerve, you can *make* your own good auction. You find an auction that is taking place at a farm out in the back country somewhere; for such an auction the auctioneer puts up arrows directing people in from the main road. A couple of hours before the auction begins, you go around changing the directions in which the arrows point.

It is always good, of course, if you can arrange the arrows so that everybody doesn't wind up at a dead end; people are very likely to get angry over having to back up in a crazy, backwards caravan over a couple of miles of dirt road. I saw this happen once, and you can believe me that a few of us were a little more than slightly mad.

The best way, if you can manage it, is to direct the people back onto the highway at a point ahead of the place where they see the first arrow pointing off the highway. This way they will keep going in circles all afternoon.

Now, I won't say it was Heaton Vorse's granddaddy that changed the arrows that day Uncle George backed up over two miles of dirt road. On the other hand, I won't say it wasn't, and let's just leave it at that. He's gone to his reward anyway, and there isn't anything anybody can do about it if it was he.

Incidentally, Heaton's granddaddy Hiram had a wonderful growth of corn on his farm one summer. One day a neighbor dropped by and they both sat down on the steps to not talk for a while. Finally the neighbor took his piece of straw out of his mouth and said, "That sure is a nice crop you got there this year, Hiram." Hiram thought it over for a while, scratched the back of his head a little, and said, "Ayup. Them's the kind of crops sure beat hell out of the soil."

A man with the nerve to pull one like that sure isn't above changing the directions of a few arrows!

A final serious word about buying at auctions. Never buy anything unless you look it over carefully before it goes up on the podium. Get to the auction an hour before it starts and inspect the pieces that interest you from close up. This is always allowed, because it is a rule laid down by the state when they give the auctioneer his license. But there aren't any rules that say he has to see every crack in a china bowl or be able to tell the difference between cherry wood and poplar that has been stained a nice dark-brownish red. In fact, he is more prone to little oversights like these than any other class of individual in the world. You might say that his very living is based on having poor eyesight.

For additional sources see the chapter called "The Gentle Art of Acquisition" in *The Furniture Doctor*.

SILK PURSES FROM SOW'S EARS

Before we get to the business of selling our loot, let's consider a few of the things we can do to it to increase its value. These are so many and varied that the following list is barely a beginning. Besides, most of the things I know about have to do with furniture—or with items made of wood.

Obviously, the first thing is patching up veneers, regluing, refinishing. That, I believe, is a subject that I have fully covered in a previous work.

But how about modifying things? A small commode with its single drawer and two doors that swing open is not nearly as useful and desirable a piece as a small chest of drawers. What you do, then, is take the doors off and fill the cupboard space with two drawers. Admittedly this will take the average amateur cabinetmaker a few hours, maybe four or five. But if your commode was of pine, say, what was once a hard-to-move item at even as low a price as twenty dollars (refinished) is now a quick sale at thirty-five dollars.

How about taking an ordinary plank-seat kitchen chair and putting rockers on? This takes a band saw to cut the rockers, of course. But you can also do it with one of those light little saber saws. Or even with a saber-saw attachment that fits on a quarter-inch drill.

For some reason, people like the bases of old cottage-pine chests to be cut in curves. That's another place that a saber-saw comes in handy, a lot handier than a band saw.

Learn to put new cane in chairs. The people who advertise caning supplies will send you directions. The same goes for rush bottoms. Both are a lot easier to do than they look.

You know those commode chairs that look something like a Boston rocker without the rockers? People think they are funny and laugh at them in your shop—but nobody, not even Gimbels, ever buys one. Not even at five dollars. But if you fill in the hole in the seat, smooth it over with plastic wood and paint it black, then knock out the box under the seat, and finally put it on rockers . . . well, I saw one sell for forty-five dollars!

Along the same lines, it is always good to collect pieces of tables: legs without a top, tops without bottoms, stray leaves, and just plain flat boards. And large breadboards or other cutting boards. Many's the fine old antique that has come into being this way, and the markup, of course, is terrific. One old fellow I knew over in New York State had them all neatly stacked—legs and frames on one side of his barn, tops and leaves on the other. He was too lazy to do any carpentry to fit them together. He just waited until he picked up something that was a perfect fit to something he already had "in stock."

Similar to the problem of the commode chair—"potty-chair," as it is usually called—is the washstand with a round hole cut in the top to hold a washbasin. Once in a while you can sell one, but this is a pretty special piece in interior decoration. On the other hand, if the handyman in your crew can replace the top with a solid piece of wood, the piece will be worth twice as much and move ten times as fast because more people can use it.

People have been cutting down marble-top Victorian tables for a long time now, because modern interior decoration calls for lower tables. But you can do the same thing with many another table of the Victorian Era. For instance, those long tables people used to have in entrance halls. These ugly ducklings are really striking pieces when cut down to coffee-table height.

Collect any pieces of marble you see, too. They can be cut to fit pieces whose tops have been broken. They can replace wooden tops on Victorian oak pieces also, thereby raising the value of, say, an ordinary oak chest of drawers from five dollars to forty-five dollars. I saw a fellow buy a whole bedroom set that had been retopped this way. And he *knew* what had been done.

Learning to use wood stain is fundamental. Everybody knows that a table that looks as though it *might* be cherry is better than one that certainly is pine or poplar.

I suppose people are still throwing Empire chests into lakes to soak the veneer off them so they can be sold as massive Early American pine. Empire should be getting scarce enough so that this nefarious process will be grinding to a halt.

Frames will move a lot faster, too—and they usually don't move at all—if you cut pieces of glass to fit them and put in any old print. It moves the old prints faster, too. Let's face it, people are lazy.

Old paintings can make money if you can overcome the awe of them that most people have. And let's face it—nobody wants big paintings any more. An appraiser may tell you that some three-by-five-foot canvas of a rustic scene is worth $150. But if you have it around for a year—or five years —you will find that nobody even asks you what you want for it. And if we are going to be realistic about things, that makes it worth precisely *zero*. Every painting, however, has a little area where something is going on—even if it is only a cow meditating under a tree. If you cut that area out and put it in a frame of reasonable size, you have something that will sell. You can use some old wood to make the new stretcher, but that isn't important. True, a buyer can see what has been done, but practically all people hang their pictures on the wall with the painted side of the canvas out, and that's the side most of them care about.

I once got six pictures out of one by cutting it up. All right, so I'm a direct descendant of Attila the Hun. I'm sorry I brought the subject up in the first place.

Not really. In fact, I think I'll get something else out of my system. And that's the business about how only a real, expert restorer should ever clean an oil painting. You know who spreads that story? Who else? Real, expert restorers, that's who. But let's face it. Very few oil paintings are worth as much as a real expert you-know-what would charge to clean them.

Long ago I found out what they do, and I never ruined a painting. I've turned a lot of ghastly black smudges into salable pictures, which I think anyone else could do.

The first step is to understand that an antique oil painting is made up of five layers:

1. The canvas.
2. A sizing or coating of chalky white paint.
3. The oil paints themselves.
4. A protective coating of shellac. It is called varnish, and people will insist that it's varnish, but it is still shellac. The confusion arises from the fact that in the old days shellac

was called "spirit varnish." And even today, some painters use the term "varnish" for any protective coating. Now, this top coat of shellac is a great break; it makes it possible to clean a painting. As any schoolboy knows, shellac will dissolve in denatured alcohol, and hardened oil paints will not. Let's not rush things, however.

5. A layer of grime or greasy dust, or whatever you want to call it. Sometimes this layer of dirt lies on the surface of the shellac, but more often it has worked its way into the shellac.

All right. That's the picture. To clean it, we work from the top down, trying the following things until one of them works:

First: Dust the surface well with a dry paint-brush.

Second: Wipe the surface gently with a soft cloth dampened with water—only dampened, not wet. In some cases this will take off quite a lot of dirt. In others it will have no effect. If nothing happens—stop. Never apply pressure. The idea is to dissolve, not to scrape. If a gentle wiping doesn't lighten the picture, it means that in this case the layer of dirt is not in a water-soluble base. Therefore, we try something else.

Third: Let the surface dry for a few minutes, then pour onto it pure turpentine and let it soak in for five minutes. The turpentine will not dissolve the shellac but it will soften greasy grime. After five minutes, flood the surface of the painting with turpentine again, then stand it on end to let the turpentine drain off. Gently blot up the remaining turpentine wetness with facial tissue. This will invariably bring off a good deal of dirt, which you will see on the tissue. Repeat the whole process until the tissue stops getting dirty.

So far you haven't taken even the slightest chance of hurting the painting, and about half the paintings treated this way will be much lighter by now.

Fourth: In case the grime has worked its way into the protective coating of shellac, the problem is to remove the shellac without damaging the hardened oil paint beneath it. Therefore, we let the painting dry overnight after its turpentine bath, and the next day we go about removing the dirty shellac. We work on a small area of the surface at a time—an area about the size of the palm of your hand—starting in an uninteresting corner of the picture, because this makes us feel safer. Onto this area we pour a teaspoonful of denatured alcohol. (Do *not* use rubbing alcohol, which has about 30 per cent water in it. This is absolutely *verboten*, because water can seep through minute cracks in the oil paint and soften the white ground underneath, causing the oil paint to flake off.)

After the alcohol has soaked into the film of shellac for about half a minute, swish it around with a camel's-hair brush or the kind used for painting with water colors. Then squeeze out the brush and use it as a sponge to pick up the alcohol. With the alcohol, of course, will come the dirty shellac, and if this procedure doesn't brighten your picture, nothing will. Something has happened to darken the oil paints themselves.

Assuming it does work, however, you simply repeat the process over the whole painting—continuing to work on only a few square inches at a time. This will keep you busy for a couple of evenings.

The final step is to let the painting dry a couple of weeks and to apply a fresh coat of varnish over the oils. Use *only* varnish sold for this purpose in an art-supply store. This is also applied with a soft camel's-hair brush—though some art-supply stores now sell it in spray cans. It is a good idea to apply a coat of varnish to the back of the painting. This will prevent moisture from getting into the undercoating or ground and causing the oils to crack or flake off.

"STUFF FOR SALE"

We have opened our shop, bought our antiques, and fixed them up when possible. This brings us to the fine art of selling

them, or the area of why antique dealers hate people. I have
lived on both sides of the battle line, and I must admit that
basically my feelings are with the dealer.

I remember the summer I talked my Uncle George into
opening an antique shop. In addition to his workshop, he had
a small barn down by the road. During the spring we put some
old windows and a door in the front of it, lined the walls with
shelves, ran an electric cable down to it, and finally filled it up
around the middle of June with a bunch of junk that even the
famous Bob Harpin wouldn't try to sell. (And that's saying
a lot!)

Naturally, since we didn't care one way or another, we did
fine. There is nothing that will sell stuff as well as that old
Yankee take-it-or-leave-it attitude. Besides, that attitude came
naturally to both of us, and we practiced on each other and
got it down pat. Our real triumph came—and this gets back to
the point about people—over a brass lamp with a white glass
shade that we had marked at what we considered a very
reasonable $19.50.

Well, one woman kept coming in and looking at that thing
every day for a week. Never bought anything but always gave
the lamp another inspection to see if she could find something
the matter with it. She always came alone, and that meant that
one of us had to take a trip out to the barn to stand around
with her. It got so we dreaded to see her car pull up.

Finally the weekend came, and there was a bunch of people
in the shop. Uncle George and I were both in the antique
shop playing don't-give-a-damn Yankee to beat the band.
You'd have thought we were retired members of Actors'
Equity. You never heard so much nasal drawling and "ayups"
and "nayups."

Well, inevitably her car pulled up, and this time she had
her husband with her. Up for the weekend, of course. Uncle
George and I looked at each other across the room. Right
away I shook my head from side to side to convey the message

that I was only a growing boy of forty and this was a job for a real grown-up Yankee.

So the most cantankerous Yankee of them all went over to talk with the woman and her husband. Seems she'd brought her husband to look at the lamp. He looked at it awhile, and it was obvious he didn't think much of it. But she kept at him, and after a while the man allowed as how he was interested in buying the thing, but he wanted to know if Uncle George wouldn't let him have something off on the price.

Now, as that lamp had cost my Uncle George all of $3.50, he naturally was reluctant to come down on his price of a mere $19.50. Especially since he'd already wasted about six hours with the fellow's wife. So Uncle George hemmed and hawed awhile—and I could see he was mad as blazes and trying to think of something really devastating to say. But finally he just nodded his head in that thoughtful manner he picked up the time he saw Raymond Massey play Abe Lincoln in the movies, and said very meekly, "Well, I'll have to ask my wife." And with that he walked out of the shop.

I got done with the people I had been talking to and went back to our workshop. Uncle George was there, and I was there, so naturally we didn't either of us say anything, because you're never supposed to mention anything like that until a year or so goes by. But after waiting around a couple of hours, danged if the couple didn't come back into our sawdust pile. The man was a little testy by now, so he walked up to Uncle George and said with his volume turned up just a little, "Well, what did your wife say?"

Uncle George turned slowly and looked at him, shifted an imaginary cud of tobacco, and said, "I ain't ast her yit."

At this the poor fellow blew a tube (as who wouldn't) and hollered back in his best imitation Yankee accent, "Well, why the hell ain't cha?"

Uncle George just looked at him calmly while he shifted his

cud to his other cheek. "I cain't," he said. "She ain't due back from Europe till September."

Well, you've heard of men sputtering? That poor fellow blew like a whale. I doubled up, myself, and got down on my knees in back of one of our benches. I knew that if I let a single hoot out, Uncle George wouldn't speak to me for a week. Finally I got my breath and peeked over the top of the workbench, and, as I expected, the professional Yankee, himself, was calmly turning a piece of maple on one of our lathes. So I put on my stone face and went to work, and neither of us said a word until it was time for supper.

There aren't enough Uncle Georges to go around. Never have been and never will be. So the buyers win most of these little encounters. I can tell you, though, a way to settle the problem of children roaming around and smashing things. All you have to do is put up a sign that says: NO CHILDREN. Of course, it is pretty superfluous, because few people bring children to antique shops, and even fewer children will stay in them. The real advantage in having such a sign is that every once in awhile someone will say to you, "Why, Mr. So-and-so, don't you like children?"

Then you get to say, in the immortal words of W. C. Fields, "How do you mean? Fried or boiled?"

Waning serious for a change, and assuming that you are located where people get to see your merchandise, the basic problem of selling antique stock is setting the right price. This is because the people who buy antiques come from some tradition of interest in them. Besides being sophisticated, they are incurable shoppers and bargain hunters. Many's the time a customer knows far more about the value of a thing than the dealer who is trying to sell it to him.

So, my definition of "the right price" is 2 per cent less than the general public in your area is willing to pay for an item. If you price it at thirty-four dollars and the public's evaluation of its worth is thirty-five dollars, you are going to sell it if you don't say a word to the people who come into your shop but are just halfway polite.

The right price hasn't anything whatever to do with what you invested in the piece. If you have thirty dollars in it, the right price is still thirty-four dollars. If you have five dollars in it, the right price is thirty-four dollars.

Of course, I am speaking of your "adventure" purchase, that is, the buying of things on your own as opposed to things you got from a picker or wholesaler who has used his knowledge to establish a price at the wholesale level—about 50 per cent of what you should get.

You ask how I decide how much the public is willing to pay for an item. Well, there are a number of ways:

1. Make friends with other dealers by exchanging favors, and then pick their minds. Almost all of them will be glad to help you if you are a serious applicant for membership in their fraternity. They know they are crazy to be in the business and always like to have companionship. Actually, they are the nicest and friendliest people in the world.

2. Find a library (or friend) with a file of *Hobbies* magazine. It is jam-packed with advertisements of antiques for sale. It is the national market place, where prices are established. Each issue contains ads for around a thousand separate items. The ads are placed by thirty or so dealers, every one of whom is a realist about getting the most he can and, on the other hand, not pricing himself out of the market. (For instance, Trader Bob Harpin has been running a full-page ad in the book for fifteen years. To date he has listed—usually with photographs—over 6000 items. And sold even more, because many times he has had two or three of the same item.)

There are still a few dealers around who put inflated prices on everything. No matter what you show any interest in, they can offer you a "special buy." But this sort of thing is a sure way to convince potential regular customers of their lack of integrity. Dealers who do this don't stay in business long. The simple fact they overlook is that people who buy antiques are not dumb. You can fool them once or twice, or maybe for a season, but not for very long.

Incidentally, on the subject of pricing items for sale, be prepared for thieving customers, too. Don't think that dealers who are always talking about shoplifters are a little paranoid. It's a real problem, and the only solution is glass cases for small items. Then all you have to watch out for are the women who come into your shop as slender young brides and leave half an hour later in the eighth month of pregnancy. (No fooling—it happens!)

Another practice to avoid is having some "nice young girl from the neighborhood" watch your shop while you are off on a buying trip. The girl may be fine, but she is fair game for the "label switchers." These are the jokers who switch the labels on three-dollar items and eighteen-dollar items to get themselves some real bargains.

SOME ANGLES ON SELLING

Most people don't realize that there are other ways to sell antiques besides over the counter in the shop behind the bay window with the little panes and the ivy crawling over the old bricks. That's what the more cynical pros in the business call an old smithy shop. (A shiny little store carrying mostly glass and china and brass at tourist prices is called a parlor shop. "Tourist prices" means city prices brought to the country for the summer.) There are ways of selling antiques that a stranger to the game might never think of. And many dealers live on one or several without having a shop at all.

FROM THE TRUCK

The one that appeals to me the most is the way Joe Patrick sells his eagles. He found out about it by accident. One day he'd been down to Providence to pick up some things from another dealer. Among the various treasures he returned with was an eagle carved out of wood and gilded. It was a reproduction, but someone had rubbed raw umber on it, and that makes anything look older. Well, the eagle looked kind of perishable, so Joe put it right on top of his load—not under his tarpaulin, but outside it, so the wings wouldn't get chafed. On his way home he pulled into a Howard Johnson's restaurant. He went in and sat at the counter in his old clothes, and before he was finished with his 3-D sandwich two different couples had come up to him and asked if they could take a closer look at his eagle. He sold it, of course, to the highest bidder. And ever since, he has never come back from Providence without one. He claims he has yet to get all the way home with it.

The moral of the story is never to cover the merchandise in your truck until it starts raining. Pile it high, and arrange it so that the small things show well. This doesn't apply only when you are at Howard Johnson's, but also whenever you go to an auction or just drive downtown. Jim Wharton tells about the time he got excited and paid $365 for a beautiful old chest of drawers at an auction. Twenty minutes after it was loaded onto his truck, he sold it for $385. Not much profit, you might say. But he points out that he made a dollar a minute. Besides that, it might have taken him a year to sell the piece out of his shop, and he'd have had his money tied up in it all that time. Moral: if you can make twenty dollars in twenty minutes, don't be a hog.

Incidentally, you might be wondering how those people in Howard Johnson's knew Joe Patrick was the dealer that belonged to the truck with the eagle on top. Easy. The dealer is always the fellow with old clothes on. That's the uniform. Somehow, people don't seem to want as much for things when they're selling to a fellow who looks poor. I know half a dozen dealers who are really rich men. And not one of them has had a suit on since the last time he had to go to a funeral.

One old fellow who once educated me out of a few hundred dollars even used to chew on a piece of straw. After our deal was closed, we rode back in his hundred-dollar automobile to his $70,000 house, where one of his servants served us a couple of cold drinks on his patio overlooking his private eight-mile-long swimming pool.

FROM THE HOUSE

Another interesting technique is called "selling from the house." This is done with better pieces only, and gets into the realm of fairly fancy salesmanship. What you do is this: when a customer looks seriously interested in, say, a small tripod table, you tell him that you have a really beautiful example of the same sort of thing in your living room. He'd love to see it, naturally, because people who buy antiques always love to see what a dealer has in his living room. Once inside, the poor customer naturally adores your table, because it is twice as good as the one in the shop. And you finally weaken and let him have it. Assuming average markups on both pieces, you naturally make twice as much money as you would if you'd sold the "bait" in the shop.

The fact that the flow of merchandise into your shop is often uneven brings up another way of selling. Let us say you've had chances to buy two "contents" within a month. Naturally you are going to have more stuff than you can fit in your shop. Also, a lot of it will be duplications or close to it. What you do is to load a pile of the junk on your truck and take it around to other dealers whose buying may not have been going so well lately. And, as the saying goes, a dealer will always make a deal. If he can't afford to buy any of your stuff at the moment, he will take it on consignment—assuming you are realistic about values and willing to split the profit with him.

Later on, if you are ever short of merchandise, you can go

back and pick the stuff up again. Better to store your excess in a place where people can see it and may buy it than to have it hidden in some secret barn.

FROM THE BARN

Speaking of secret barns, many dealers do drift into selling from them. (No accounting for taste, as the old lady said when she kissed her cow.) They pile their stuff in a barn, and soon other dealers begin stopping by your shop to see what's there and maybe do a little trading between swapping stories and news of the Rialto. These are the dealers who are taken back to the barn. Naturally, one can't sell to other dealers at much of a markup on the average. But, on the other hand, they are real buyers and very likely to take a station wagon full.

This operation is for dealers in areas where there is a lot of stuff on the market—those in or around the "depressed areas." They become wholesalers on the side. But that's the antique business. You sell whatever you can, where you can, when you can, however you can.

If you are wondering where the money is going to come from for all these operations, the incredible answer is banks. I realize that everybody knows that banks hate to lend money. One of the biggest shocks I ever got in my life was when, as a young man, I asked a banker to lend me $300 because I needed it badly and he asked me how much money I had in my savings account. I thought he was crazy. I have learned much since then. From uncle-you-know-who. For it was he who pointed out to me that there is a fine point involved. It's not that banks don't like to lend money. They just don't like to lend it to people who need it. Such people look like a bad risk to them. And banks are businesses, not welfare agencies. So, the trick is to convince the banker whose money you want that you don't really need it.

It's not hard at all. Let us say that you've just lost all your money in the stock market or at roulette or something, and your wife and you are down to your last thirty dollars cash. (This once happened to a dear friend of mine who will remain nameless.) What you do is go out and buy yourself a Stetson hat for twenty-five dollars. You know, the kind that Texas millionaires wear. With the remaining five dollars you buy five one-dollar cigars and arrange them in your breast pocket so that the labels show. It doesn't matter if neither you nor the banker smokes cigars. Entirely beside the point. But, of course, when you walk into his office you offer the banker one.

He asks you how things are going, and you say wonderful. You tell him how you have three or four deals going for you that are working out just grand. Of course, that real estate downtown that you are going to double your money on does have all your capital tied up, and you did happen to get wind of something the other day. A treasure trove. An old house that no one but you has been allowed in for the last eighty years. What a profit you could make on that deal if the bank could see its way clear to lending you a few thousand—just for a few months, of course—until your other deals resolve themselves.

The fellow I know walked out with the money. Of course, there was one other detail. He had a twenty-year reputation for being honest. Honest in the sense of always having paid his bills, I mean. Well, that's what counts to bankers.

SELLING BY MAIL

As the national interest in antiques expands, more and more selling is being done by mail. The best medium, as I have mentioned, is the fabulous *Hobbies*, available only by subscription. Send your check for $3.50 to *Hobbies*, 1006 South Michigan Ave., Chicago, Illinois 60605.

Now, selling by mail order is a little deeper than it looks on the surface. There are hidden advantages. Let's say you have six clocks, circa 1900. You just show one in the ad. If six people send checks for it, you send the first person the clock. But you send pictures (Polaroid camera, of course!) of your other clocks to the other people, and nine times out of ten they will buy.

Another point is that you are getting into correspondence with real collectors. You can find out (simply by asking) what things they are interested in, and when you come across such things you write them directly, enclosing a picture and your price. This saves the cost of advertising.

Incidentally, *Hobbies* is divided into all sorts of departments, such as guns, dolls, prints, old records and phonographs, stamps, coins, jewelry, china, gems, clocks. Everything gets covered in editorial columns and sold through the accompanying ads.

(Official statement: I have no financial interest in *Hobbies* whatsoever. I don't even have friends who work on it. It's just there and great, and I see no way to avoid raving about it.)

ANTIQUE SHOWS

When it comes to selling your merchandise through antique shows—here is where we separate the men from the boys. You have to know what people will buy, and you have to have your price just right. In a country show you may pay as little as fifty dollars for a booth. But with even such a small "nut" to make, there are also your living expenses and the fact that you can't be at your shop. In the big city shows the booths start at around $350, which means you have to run pretty fast to break even.

Many of the most successful dealers refuse to go to any shows. Life, they feel, is too short for all the packing and unpacking and tension of the whole thing. All the dealers I've met that go to a lot of shows cheerfully admit to being slightly "teched." They think of themselves as being like people who can't stay away from the race track. Of course, I'll have to admit that they are a wonderfully friendly lot. They just seem to have an abnormally low capacity for getting disturbed by anything.

On the other hand, there are other advantages to going to shows than the money you may or may not make. In the first place, you get to see a lot of things that other people think will sell, and the prices they think they can get. It's educational. At a show, everyone is willing to swap information without trying to put something over. It is like belonging to a social club, whose slogan is "Us dealers have to stick together against the world."

It is frequently suspected that at any given show the dealers sell more to each other than they do to the public. This is probably not literally true—but it is almost true. The reason is the old principle that the way to make money in the antique business is by moving things from one part of the country to another. A fellow from Maine will have things that a fellow from Maryland never gets a chance to buy at home, and vice versa. And when dealers sell to each other it is almost always at 20 per cent less than the marked price. I know this doesn't seem logical when the sale is just a single item. (For a station wagon full of stuff it would be.) As far as I can see, it is just part of the friendly feeling that we all belong to the same club. (Every one of them will deny this about himself, claiming to be a hard businessman, but you know how people are. They hate to admit that they are nice. Me too.)

AUCTIONS AGAIN

Our final and least satisfactory way of selling is through auctions. This isn't because the prices gotten don't average out to be a true reflection of market value, but because the auctioneer usually gets a 20 per cent commission.

This brings up the problem of the so-called "salted auction," in which some dealer's stock is included in the auction of a household. For some reason this isn't supposed to be done, but you know how those things are. And it beats me why people go around muttering about it. After all, the more stuff at any auction, the better an auction it is from everybody's point of view. I guess the muttering is done by the same people who are always complaining about dealers bidding the prices up at an auction—a libel that I have discussed elsewhere in these pages. There are always some people around who simply refuse to get in touch with the realities of life.

Which reminds me of the story of the two fellows who were about to be executed by a South American firing squad. They were standing there in the early morning light with their backs against the wall. The officer in charge of the firing squad came up to them with a couple of blindfolds and offered one to the first fellow. A fellow named Pedro. Well, Pedro looked the officer in the eye and refused in unprintable language, and then went on to make some equally unprintable remarks about the officer's parentage. At this point, the fellow standing next to Pedro nudged him in the ribs with his elbow and said, "What did you say that for? Aren't we in enough trouble already?"

All I can add is: Why go into the antique business anyway? Aren't you in enough trouble already?

PRICE GUIDE

The following are the values of the pieces illustrated in this book at the time this edition went to press. For a general commentary on the value of Victoriana, see the preface to this edition on page ix. It's called "See Price Guide in Back of Book" and it tells you to look here. Which is probably going too far again, but I don't want anybody to get lost.

1. This rarer type of spool bed is still much undervalued at the usual $75 plus that it commands in the rough. Refinished and widened to take a modern-size mattress, it still goes for only $175—which makes it a real sleeper, whether you can stand puns or not.

2. More plentiful than the preceding bed, this style is, on the other hand, harder to remodel, and so, refinished and remodeled to take a modern mattress, it also comes out $175. It has doubled in price in five years and will easily do the same in the next five.

3. With the original paint job, this is up from $20 to $40. If the original paint job was in such bad condition that the piece had to be refinished (it's pine), put the price at $45 refinished. Both prices should double in five years.

4. Whether it is made of cherry and maple or mahogany-veneered pine or all pine, the refinished price is around $150 for the two-drawer model, $110 for the one-drawer. It is already well up there, and future price rises will be comparatively moderate.

5. With either a good deal of the original decoration remaining, or expertly redecorated, these chairs go for about $110, a set of four for $500.

6. Say $45 with most of the decoration rubbed off. In fine original condition or quietly redecorated, $85. An earlier version with the wooden seat curving up at the back is called a Salem rocker and is worth a little more—$85 to $110.

7. Currently up to about $25 in the rough, but only beginning to climb on the sophisticated big-city market. Don't be surprised to see one gilded and antiqued, with a pink velvet seat, for $75 in a decorator's shop even now. These things "come in" overnight.

8. These chairs are a little bit earlier than Hitchcock, as evidenced by more traces of Sheraton design. A completely redecorated set of six recently brought $600. Six in pretty good original decoration would be fifty per cent more.

9. One of the more standard models among Fancy chairs, these so-called Bamboo Sheratons bring $60 as found, $90 reglued, reseated, and refinished. (The refinishing is easy—just wipe them off with a cloth dipped in alcohol.)

10. A standard piece—$75 to $85 refinished.

11. Five years ago these were top of the heap at $85. Currently they are $150 in the rough, $210 refinished. Such prices make it profitable to fake these pieces—by putting the dry-sink top on an ordinary commode or even putting doors and top on any "box." But nobody seems to care whether they are fake or not, and so even when the patchwork is obvious, they still go for the same prices.

12. These have risen to $45 in the rough, $85 refinished. They are $135 to $150 on the West Coast.

13. About $50 in the rough, $85 refinished.

14. In the rough with the hole in the top, $30. With a new solid top put on and refinished, up to $75.

15. Up to $35 refinished and recaned—and what a bargain-basement bargain they are at that price.

16. Because these are so useful, they have shot up to $40 in the rough, $85 and up refinished. The big spread isn't because they're hard to refinish. It's because of an information gap between pickers who sell them to dealers and the dealers who sell them to real people.

17. $15 in the rough, $40 reglued and refinished.

18. $25 in the rough, $45 refinished. Add another $20 if solid top has been installed.

19. The painted pine Cottage version goes for $65 in the rough, $140 refinished. The older Empire version, with some solid mahogany and the rest mahogany veneer on pine, is $110 in the rough, $185 refinished. Everybody loves a desk, but these are a little big for most people.

20. In Pennsylvania, where it is most often found, this chair with the distinctive "bootjack" back is about $25 in the rough, $45 refinished.

21. $50 in the rough, $80 refinished.

22. In pine $55 in the rough, $110 tightened up and refinished. A walnut one with several leaves will run to $185 refinished. A refinished cherry with leaves, $220.

23. $45 in the rough, $85 refinished.

24. Same as preceding commode, but where original decoration is in good condition or the drawer and door fronts are burl-veneered, the value of such pieces is moving up so rapidly you need a weekly quotation.

25. Found in good condition—all the veneer intact and joints tight —$125. Double that if it is reupholstered in fairly good material.

26. Make this $150 in good condition, $300 reupholstered. If that seems low, it's because not many people want pieces of this size in their houses.

27. Same as preceding couch. Because of their large, clumsy size, these three pieces are about the only ones that are not rising in price along with the rest of Victoriana.

28. $85 in the rough, $125 refinished.

29. Currently a real bargain at $45 in the rough, $80 refinished.

30. A lighter chair than the preceding—$35 in the rough and $65 refinished.

31. $55 as found, $95 or $100 refinished and with seat recovered.

32. About $55 if found with veneer in good condition. After regluing and refinishing, only $95, and the demand is weak, illustrating again that bulky pieces are not the winners in this generation of antiques. (As they are, for instance, in the popular French styles—all the way into French Empire.)

33. With finish restored, but the works not repaired, these are $85. Repair of the works runs about $125. More often the works are removed and the piece made into a desk, which pushes the price up to $125 to $135. But for some reason these pieces are nowhere nearly as popular as other desks. A slow mover in any version.

34. Here's one big piece that people do like. Since Empire secretaries are so easy to refinish, you aren't likely to find one on the market in the rough. Refinished and with the veneer all patched up, they go for $350 to $400. Pieces like this aren't found standing around in barns, either—too hard to move out of the house—so don't even try looking for one in the rough.

35. About $85 when found in good condition, $150 refinished.

36. A slow market on these leaves them at $85 in good condition, $125 refinished. Beats me!

37. These terribly useful things stand at the top of the price scale in Empire. $285 if found in good condition, $385 reglued and refinished. People like them, and that makes all the difference.

38. Almost as good as the preceding butler's desk, this secretary goes for $200 in the rough, $275 refinished.

39. With a solid mahogany top, $50 refinished.

40. Refinished, $75.

41. Refinished, these are $45 to $65, depending on size.

42. Here is a typical doubler. Up from $55 to $110 in the last six years.

43. Frames on pieces like these have always gotten so loose that they have to be taken completely apart for regluing. Then, after refinishing and reupholstering, the going price is $350 for average material.

44. Ditto.

45. Ditto.

46. Again after necessary regluing, refinishing, and reupholstering, these are twice what they were six years ago—now $165.

47. Ditto—and now $185 reglued, refinished, and reupholstered.

48. Same as above—$175.

49. Same as above—$175.

50. Refinished and reseated, still *very* undervalued at current market price of $75.

51. Ditto—at $35 to $40.

52. Refinished and reupholstered, $650 as I write this, going to be $850, etc., in a hurry.

53. Ditto.

54. Currently $350, and I wish I had a dozen in the attic.

55. Up from $300 to $600 in the last six years. These belong in museums, or will pretty soon. People will laugh at this (low) price in a few years.

56. Here's an incredible sleeper. Half a dozen dealers have told me they would pay $100 to $200 for one of these. If I had one, I wouldn't sell it for less than $1500. It is a very rare piece of our artistic history.

57. In the first edition of this book I noted that a set of four of these sold for "as high as $160." I wish I'd bought them. And I'd go $800 for them today in calm certainty that I'd double my money in a few years.

58. This, I was told six years ago, was worth $300. And there are dealers who still think so. Right now it's a wide-open situation, but if it isn't worth $2500 in five years, I'll kiss your poodle in Macy's window.

59. With the walnut top, $85 at most. With the marble top, $140. Both still way underpriced.

60. Incredibly enough, you could have gotten a smallish version of this piece for $60 five years ago. Today it is $125—in the marble-topped version—and is due to triple in price in the next five years.
   Variation: The painted pine version was $40 five years ago. It is impossible to quote a current market price because they are becoming worth their weight in gold as irreplaceable Americana.

61. These have not risen much. Currently only about $65. Not due to rise much, because so many of them were made, and shelves full of little things don't relate much to modern décor.

62. Up from $65 to $225 in six years. Will double in another five.

63. From $45 to $150 in six years. Will double in five more.

64. Texas millionaires or some millionaires have turned on to these headboards (formerly white elephants because of their mammoth size), and they are now sold for $600 to that trade. Now, let's see —if you had bought ten for $40 apiece five years ago . . .

65. Up from $70 to $185, refinished and reupholstered, in the last six years.

66. Up from $75 to $225 in the last six years.

67. The same dealer who sold these for $65 six years ago sells all he can get for $195 today.

68. Again the same dealer sold these for $65 to $85 six years ago. Today they move fast at $265.

69. A cheap mass-produced piece, even this is up from $25 to $65.

70. If they are high enough to be used as an end table, these are $65 in the rough, $175 refinished in oak. In walnut, they are $225 refinished. The low ones are still available at $30 in the rough, so you can see what a tremendous difference modern utility makes.

71. Would you believe I priced this at five different dealers at $45 five years ago? Today the same dealers are getting $200 and over.

72. These chairs have come into demand, rising to $125 refinished and reupholstered. They will soar up from there as people come to understand this sort of thing.

73. You had to buy these in the rough—for $35—five years ago. Currently $185 refinished and reupholstered.

74. I could cry to think that Joe Patrick tried to sell me this desk for $75 six years ago. Currently Bob Jenkins of Leonard's Antiques in Seekonk, Massachusetts, sells them for $650. With the cylinder roll top they are only $435. (I am quoting Bob Jenkins here to demonstrate that this isn't just some crazy New York City price. Jenkins sells to interior decorators across the country.)

75. These are up from $85 to $125 reupholstered.

76. I fell flat on my face when I predicted six years ago that this piece would never be popular. The four-foot-high one has jumped from $35 to $125. In the ten-foot-six-inch version they go for $500 to interior decorators.

77. Even these former "give aways" are now $45 in the rough, and in New York City a four-piece bedroom set in this style—all oak—goes for $165 stripped and oiled.

78. Ditto.

79. Up in six years from $45 to $145.

80. Up in six years from $15 to $30. Why have they only doubled, when the preceding piece tripled? Because the free-standing corner shelves fit in better with current taste in interior decoration than hanging shelves do. I have spoken.

81. Up from $35 to $75 in six years.

82. Here, not only did I fall flat on my face again, but a fantastic price rise has occurred. Six years ago these were $35 in the rough, and reupholstered ones were not to be found. Today the interior-decorator shops consider them gems. And so must their customers,

who pay as high as $850 for them, rebuilt, refinished, and reupholstered in fancy tapestry or velvet.

83. Same as with the preceding piece. Found only in the rough at $20 around Providence six years ago—and usually hauled in from a dump—these now go for $295 rebuilt, refinished, and reupholstered.

84. From $12 in the rough and from the dump six years ago to $60 refinished today.

85. From $30 in the rough six years ago to $150 reglued, refinished, and reupholstered today.

86. From $5 in the rough six years ago to $45 refinished today.

87. From $7 in the rough six years ago to $30 refinished today.

88. Here we go again: from $15 in the rough then to $150 reupholstered now.

89. From $6 in the rough then to $60 recaned and refinished today.

90. One of the few weak numbers in this section. It was $12 in the rough six years ago, and it has risen only to $40 in the rough.

91. In wood, these have risen from $40 to $80. In brass, from $125 to $350.

92. Originals have gone up from $45–$65 to $125 plus.

93. Around $125.

94. Around $100.

95. Around $200.

96. Around $175 electrified.

97. Around $70.

98. Around $150.

99. Up from $30 to $75 with original finish in good condition.

100. Up from $25 to $125 with original finish and in good condition. Should double in two years, may be doing it next week.

101. Up from $25 to $125, and again may be doubling next week.

102. These all seem to have rotted away. If you find one preserved, by some miracle, I still don't know who would buy it. I'd try the

Smithsonian Institution in Washington, D.C., and the Metropolitan Museum of Art in New York City.

103. Ditto.

104. Still ugly and still not "in." Nevertheless, pieces like this stripped and oiled are worth $50, and I suppose they are due to rise as wildly as Eastlake has.

105. Ditto.

106. Ditto, but only $25.

107. Six years ago everyone thought it was silly that these were up to $45, refinished, in New York City. Now they are up to $120, refinished, everywhere. Also $150 with leaves, and one with ornate feet cut down to cocktail-table height recently sold in California for $350. But that's California—the most expensive state in the country to live in.

108. The walnut ones date as far back as the 1890s and go for $185, refinished, anywhere. The oak ones go for that much or higher in New York City, where people don't really know anything about antiques—just what is currently fashionable.

109. This table doesn't seem to appeal to anybody, and so it can still be had for only $35 refinished.

110. Another item with little popular appeal. Yours, refinished, for only $75.

111. Sold recently for $350.

112. $25 refinished.

113. Refinished $75.

114. Refinished, these are up from $75 to $175.

115. Refinished, up from $75 to $225.

116. Up from $6 to $25.

117. They break too easily, so only about $10.

118. Up from $4 six years ago to about $35 refinished and recaned. A set of four is $150. Will double or triple in next five years, or my name isn't George Grotz.

119. A drug on the market—so still only worth about $10.

120. Have really come in. Up from $22 in the rough to $195 refinished and reupholstered.

121. Up from $15 to $35. Are these the antiques of the future? I hope not, but who knows?

122. Once a piece of junk always a piece of junk. $10, and I suppose I'm falling on my face again.

123. Dealers have made a lot of money on junk like this, which is up from what I considered an insane $22 five years ago to a nice $65. Probably will double in next six years.

124. All clocks are up a lot, and this has risen from $25 to $125 refinished.

125. Up from $25 to $65 if found in good condition.

126. Currently $40 to $50 each. A flood of reproductions on the market has kept them from rising much higher.

127. I predicted these would rise a lot, and they did. From $25 five years ago to $175 today, up to $300 for really ornate ones.

128. Various designs range from $150 (this one) to $350 for large and beautiful horns or rare mechanisms.

129. Up from $35 to $125.

130. Up from $500 to $2000 and on their way to being worth their weight in gold. Will triple in five years.

131. Currently a steal at $800. Will be worth $3500 in five years or my name isn't Harry Winston.

132. Up from $45 to $200. They haven't risen higher because these were mass produced and given away to people who signed up to have electricity brought into their houses.

INDEX

U

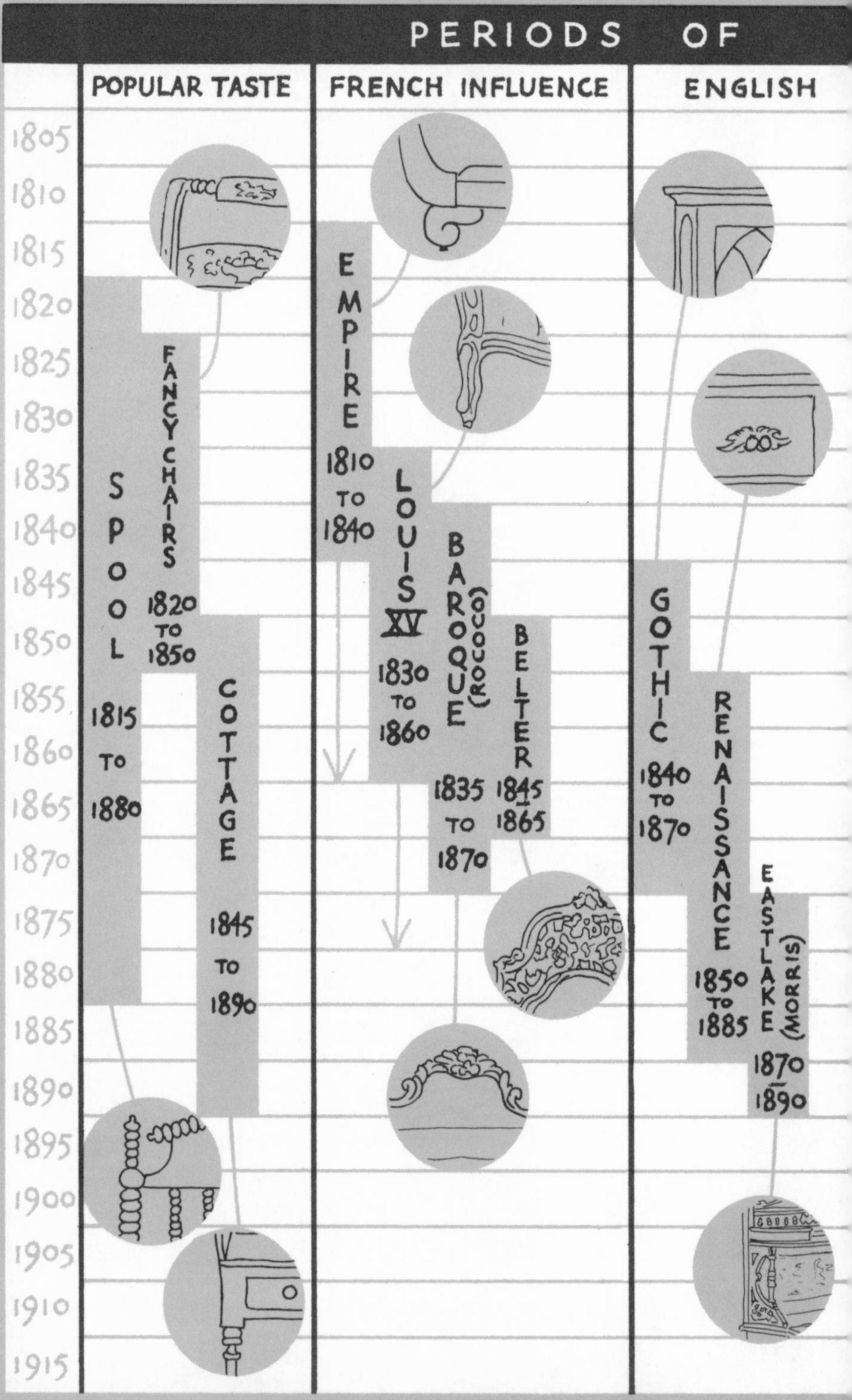

PERIODS OF

| POPULAR TASTE | FRENCH INFLUENCE | ENGLISH |

POPULAR TASTE

FANCY CHAIRS
1820 TO 1850

SPOOL
1815 TO 1880

COTTAGE
1845 TO 1890

FRENCH INFLUENCE

EMPIRE
1810 TO 1840

LOUIS XV
1830 TO 1860

BAROQUE (ROCOCO)

BELTER
1845 TO 1865

1835 TO 1870

ENGLISH

GOTHIC
1840 TO 1870

RENAISSANCE
1850 TO 1885

EASTLAKE (MORRIS)
1870 TO 1890

1805
1810
1815
1820
1825
1830
1835
1840
1845
1850
1855
1860
1865
1870
1875
1880
1885
1890
1895
1900
1905
1910
1915